Seminar on

Personal Identification in Mass Disasters

Report of a seminar held in Washington, D.C.,
9-11 December 1968, by arrangement between
the Support Services of the Department of the Army
and the Smithsonian Institution

T. D. Stewart, Editor

National Museum of Natural History
Smithsonian Institution
City of Washington
1970

*Authors of papers delivered at a seminar
held at the Smithsonian Institution, Washington, D.C.,
9-11 December 1968*

Sidney R. Galler
Eugene Giles
Leo R. Goldbaum
Howard S. Grob
Vincent P. Guinn
W. W. Howells
Ellis R. Kerley
Geoffrey T. Mann
A. Keith Mant
Thomas W. McKern
Col. D. F. Munster
Wesley A. Neep
Mildred Trotter
D. Gentry Steele
T. D. Stewart
Hobart R. Wood

Acknowledgment is made of the
support of the Department of the Army
and the U.S. Army Research and
Development Command under
Contract DADA 17-69-C-9045.

Contents

Foreword

List of Faculty and Registrants

INTRODUCTORY REMARKS

Welcome to the Smithsonian. *Sidney R. Galler*

Greetings from the Support Services. *Col. D. F. Munster*

SELECTED PAPERS

Foreword

It is the established policy of the American government to see that all deceased American military personnel are identified as far as possible. As will appear in the course of this report, the efforts of the Army, through its responsible representatives, to identify the deceased servicemen from World War II and the Korean War have led to notable improvements in the techniques of personal identification used today, not only by the Army itself but by forensic agencies throughout the world. In the present Vietnam conflict, the Army's ability to recover casualties more quickly than heretofore reduces the scale of the personal identification problem. Nevertheless, all those engaged in this sensitive operation are keenly aware of the need to promote further advances in identification techniques while, at the same time, to keep up-to-date on developments occurring elsewhere.

Thoughts of this sort were in the minds of C. T. Noll, Lt. Col. R. F. Albera, W. M. Annetti, and Frank Eskridge, who constituted a delegation from the Office of the Chief of Support Services, Department of the Army, and who came to see me on 8 May 1968, about the possibility of organizing an identification seminar within the calendar year. As a result of our discussion, Col. C. A. Shaunesey, Jr., then Chief of Support Services, addressed a letter to S. Dillon Ripley, Secretary of the Smithsonian Institution, which reads in part:

> Once again the Department of the Army turns to the Smithsonian Institution for support and help in connection with one of its most important current responsibilities, the care of deceased military personnel in Vietnam, and the return of the remains to this country for final interment. Every aspect of the mission is important and must be accomplished promptly and appropriately, but the fundamental and most sensitive phase of the work is identification—the fulcrum upon which the integrity of the entire program rests.
>
> While we believe that accepted scientific techniques and procedures are being applied in our identification laboratory in Vietnam, we wish to have the benefit of current, expert, unbiased, and disinterested guidance from specialists in all phases of identification. Hence our proposal that the Smithsonian Institution conduct a seminar on the identification of war dead during the calendar year 1968. The results of a seminar would, as a minimum, permit reassurances that all possible steps are being taken in the identification process—in short, this would represent a backup vote for the Department of Army from the scientific community. We see, however, a broader purpose and, looking to the future, believe such a meeting would tend to increase the dwindling interest in this field, permit the development of recommendations for research, and hopefully yield a breakthrough immediately applicable to our war dead program. The following suggestions represent our general thinking on the project.
>
> 1. The seminar should give broad treatment to the entire range of identification specialities. While emphasis should be placed upon problems related to the identification of war dead, and must treat both soft and hard tissue cases, the

seminar guidelines should be broad rather than restrictive and should encourage a free exchange of ideas and concepts.

2. The Army would rely entirely on the Institution's recommendations on participation, but would favor broad representation from the academic community, selected municipal police and pathological groups, the Federal Bureau of Investigation, and other federal agencies.

3. The record of all papers presented, subsequent discussions, conclusions, and recommendations should be printed, preferably by the Smithsonian, for distribution to participants and libraries.

4. Attendance at the sessions should be controlled and publicity should be limited to any releases deemed appropriate and beneficial to the agencies concerned at the conclusion of the seminar.

The Army has had a long association with the Smithsonian through Dr. T. Dale Stewart, whose consultation and advice over the years have been of tremendous value—a genuine public service. In brief informal conversations, Dr. Stewart has indicated a willingness to cooperate on the proposed seminar.

If the proposal meets with your approval, the Department of the Army will reimburse the Institution for the costs incurred. . . .

. . . we would be grateful to receive your reaction to the proposal—hopefully, your general approval and your agreement to specific detailed planning by representatives of the Institution and the Army.

Following Mr. Ripley's wholehearted endorsement of the proposal, I sought advice from nearby authorities in the forensic field, especially Dr. Russell S. Fisher, Chief Medical Examiner for the State of Maryland, and Col. Edward H. Johnston, Assistant Chief, Department of Pathology, Armed Forces Institute of Pathology. The latter kindly arranged for a meeting in which we were joined by a number of his associates at the AFIP who have had extensive practical experience in identification, and who have been involved with courses in forensic pathology and forensic dentistry that are held periodically at the Institute.

Three important considerations that had a bearing on the seminar planning emerged from these consultations:

1. A book was about to appear on "Medical Investigation of Aviation Accidents" under the editorship of Dr. W. J. Reals (published by the College of American Pathologists, Chicago, Ill., 1968, 150 pp.).
2. The AFIP was preparing to hold a fall course on forensic dentistry in which the role of the dentist in mass disasters would be emphasized.
3. Most of the forensic pathologists who might be expected to attend the projected seminar lacked experience in dealing with the war dead.

Taking all this into account, I decided that it would be wise to broaden the scope of the seminar to cover mass disasters in general, but at the same time to stress the identification of war dead over that of victims from other types of disasters. Also, it seemed best to emphasize forensic anthropology and forensic pathology at the expense of forensic dentistry. The Support Services agreed to these changes. As it turned out, however, the most spectacular experiences of some of the participants had been in connection with airplane crashes, so this aspect actually received more emphasis than planned.

For the record, the printed program was as follows: *

Monday, December 9

Morning Chairman—Dr. Stewart
  9:00—10:00   Registration
10:00—10:30   Welcome. Dr. Galler and Col. Munster

---

*For full names and identification of faculty, see page 9.

10:30—11:30	Why Identify the Victims of Disasters? Mr. McEwan and Dr. Mant
11:30—12:00	General discussion
12:00— 1:45	Lunch

Afternoon Chairman—Dr. Fisher

1:45— 2:30	Organization and Personnel for Proper Identification. Mr. Doyle
2:30— 3:15	Nature and Sources of Information About Decedents for Proper Identification. Mr. L. Trotter
3:15— 4:00	The Problem of Presumptive Identification. Dr. Helpern
4:00— 4:15	Recess
4:15— 4:45	Problems Relating to Acceptance of Identified Remains by Next of Kin. Mr. Neep
4:45— 5:30	Panel Discussion of Session Papers. Dr. Fisher, Mr. Doyle, Mr. L. Trotter, Dr. Helpern, and Mr. Neep
5:30— 6:00	Recess
6:00— 8:00	Social hour and buffet supper for everyone attending seminar
8:00— 9:00	After-supper talk by Dr. Mant: Identification Involving Atrocities

Tuesday, December 10

Chairman—Dr. Greulich

9:00— 9:30	Cytological Sexing. Dr. Grob
9:30—10:00	Neutron Activation Analysis. Dr. Guinn
10:00—10:30	Detection of Drugs in Tissues. Dr. Goldbaum
10:30—10:45	General discussion
10:45—11:00	Recess
11:00—12:00	Aging from Puberty Onward. Dr. McKern and Dr. Kerley
12:00—12:15	General discussion
12:15— 2:00	Lunch
2:00— 3:15	Estimation of Stature From Long Bones. Dr. M. Trotter and Mr. Steele
3:15— 3:30	General discussion
3:30— 4:45	Multivariate Analysis for Sex and Race. Dr. Giles and Dr. Howells
4:45— 5:00	General discussion

Wednesday, December 11
WORKSHOP ON IDENTIFICATION TECHNIQUES

Director—Dr. Mann
(Cadavers in different states will be supplied. Seminar attendees will be expected to participate as required.)

9:00—12:00	Photography. Mr. Halsman and Mr. Hale
	Fingerprinting. Mr. Wittmus
	Pathological Examination. Dr. Wood and Dr. Mann
12:00— 1:00	Lunch
1:00— 5:00	Pathological Examination—continued
	Dentistry. Dr. Salley
	Anthropology. Dr. Angel and Dr. Stewart

Some of the papers on the program are not included in this report, mainly because they duplicate the material available in Dr. Real's book. The included papers, except for changes of title in some instances, follow the program listing. Since in writing the final versions of their papers, the authors were able to take the discussions into consideration, no attempt has been made to report the discussions separately. Actually, the discussions dealt for the most part with technicalities and seldom with larger issues.

At the end of the report I have added a paper, of my own, and a bibliography.

The paper is an elaboration of an osteological feature that attracted attention during the anthropological examination which concluded the seminar. The addition of a bibliography was suggested by the scarcity of references on personal identification in Dr. Real's bibliography. The latter was provided by the computer system of the National Library of Medicine (MEDLARS), and hence is restricted to the literature of the three years 1964—66. Also, only the subject categories "aviation accidents" and "space medicine" were searched. In addition to not being limited in time, my bibliography ranges the gamut of identification techniques and gives attention to those used in mass disasters.

So far as possible I have already expressed my appreciation to all involved in the seminar for their splendid cooperation. To all specifically named in this report, I am especially indebted. In addition, I am pleased to single out the following members of the staff of the Smithsonian Institution and the nature of their assistance: Dr. J. Lawrence Angel for serving as the seminar's deputy organizer, Angela Margola and Karlena Warnock for secretarial help, and John Clear for negotiating the contract with the Department of the Army.

T. D. Stewart

Faculty and Registrants

Titles and addresses are given only for the faculty, identified by the capitalization of last names. Representatives of the Support Services and Overseas Army Mortuaries are identified by asterisks.

Affholder, David J., Capt., USAF, Dover, Del.

*Albera, Richard F., Lt. Col., USA, Washington, D.C.

ANGEL, J. Lawrence, Ph.D., Curator-in-Charge, Division of Physical Anthropology, National Museum of Natural History, Smithsonian Institution, Washington, D.C.

*Annetti, William M., Washington, D.C.

Bass, Millard, M.D., Baltimore, Md.

Blackbourne, Brian D., M.D., Miami, Fla.

Bourgeois, Kenneth, Capt., USMC, Washington, D.C.

*Braden, Moyne D., Honolulu, Hawaii

Bricker, Glenn W., M.D., Ashland, N.H.

Brown, Obie, Jr., Maj., USAF, Washington, D.C.

Canfield, Thomas M., Capt., MC, USA, Washington, D.C.

Cobb, W. Montague, M.D., Washington, D.C.

*Cody, Kenneth H., Da Nang, Vietnam

Cornwell, William S., Rochester, N.Y.

Davis, Joseph H., M.D., Miami, Fla.

Dominguez, Abel M., Lt. Col., USAF, Washington, D.C.

DOYLE, Bernard C., B.A.E., LL.B., Assistant Chief, Safety Analysis and Promotion Division, Bureau of Aviation Safety, National Transportation Safety Board, Washington, D.C.

Enos, William F., M.D., Fairfax, Va.

*Eskridge, Frank, Washington, D.C.

Fatteh, Abdullah, M.D., Washington, D.C.

Feenstra, John, Concord, N.H.

Finck, Pierre A., Col., MC, USA, Washington, D.C.

Fischer, Jack E., Wheaton, Ill.

FISHER, Russell S., M.D., Chief Medical Examiner, State of Maryland, Baltimore, Md.

Fournier, Ramon L., Maj., USA, Ft. Lee, Va.

Francisco, J. T., M.D., Memphis, Tenn.

Froede, Richard C., Lt. Col., MC, USA, Washington, D.C.

GALLER, Sidney R., Ph.D., Assistant Secretary (for Science), Smithsonian Institution, Washington, D.C.

Gantner, George E., M.D., St. Louis, Mo.

GILES, Eugene, Ph.D., Assistant Professor of Anthropology, Harvard University, Peabody Museum, Cambridge, Mass.

GOLDBAUM, Leo R., Ph.D., Chief Research Toxicologist, Toxicology Branch, Armed Forces Institute of Pathology, Washington, D.C.

Gomez, Jose J., M.D., Baltimore, Md.

Green, George H., Capt., DC, USN, Washington, D.C.

GREULICH, W. W., Ph.D., Research Biologist, National Institute for Child Health and Human Development, Bethesda, Md.

GROB, Howard S., Ph.D., Assistant Professor of Physiology and Pharmacology, New York University School of Dentistry, New York, N.Y.

Gross, Elliot M., M.D., New York, N.Y.

GUINN, Vincent P., Ph.D., Technical Director, Activation Analysis Program, Gulf General Atomic, Inc., San Diego, Calif.

*Guntharp, G. O., Honolulu, Hawaii

Hackett, John F., Jr., Brooklyn, N.Y.

HALE, Lawrence W., T.Sgt., USAF, Photographer, Photographic Branch, Armed Forces Institute of Pathology, Washington, D.C.

Hall, William E. B., M.D., Waynesboro, Pa.

HALSMAN, J., Chief of the Photographic Division, Armed Forces Institute of Pathology, Washington, D.C.

Hameli, Ali Z., M.D., Wilmington, Del.

Hass, Rita, M.D., Philadelphia, Pa.

Hazelwood, Robert R., Maj., USA, Washington, D.C.

HELPERN, Milton, M.D., Chief Medical Examiner, City of New York, New York, N.Y.

Hendrix, Robert C., M.D., Ann Arbor, Mich.

Henry, Malcolm C., Ph.D., Natick, Mass.

Herrera, Gaston, M.D., Glenn Dale, Md.

Hertzberg, H. T. E., Yellow Springs, Ohio

Hester, George, Concord, N.H.

Hoffman, Frank T., Jr., Wheaton, Ill.

HOWELLS, William W., Ph.D., Professor of Anthropology, Harvard University, Peabody Museum, Cambridge, Mass.

*Hoyt, Richard A., Okinawa

Işcan, Yaşar, Washington, D.C.

Johnson, John E., M.D., Kansas City, Kan.

Johnston, Byron F., Dover, Del.

Johnston, Edward H., Col., MC, USA, Washington, D.C.

Kennemer, Christopher Earl, D.D.S., Chevy Chase, Md.

KERLEY, Ellis R., Ph.D., Associate Professor of Anthropology, University of Kansas, Lawrence, Kan.

Kielman, Edmund R., Col., MC, USA, Washington, D.C.

Knapp, Thomas A., Capt., USA, Washington, D.C.

Kornblum, Ronald N., M.D., Baltimore, Md.

Krakaur, Richard B., Col., MC, USA, Washington, D.C.

Legowik, John T., Capt., MC, USAF, Washington, D.C.

Lynch, Joseph M., Brooklyn, N.Y.

MANN, Geoffrey T., M.D., LL.B., Chief Medical Examiner, Commonwealth of Virginia, Richmond, Va.

MANT, A. Keith, M.D., Reader in Forensic Medicine, Guy's Hospital Medical School, University of London, London, England

*McCarron, Raymond D., Oakland, Calif.

McConnel, Mervin G., Maj., USA, Washington, D.C.

McEWAN, Gerald J., LL.B., Deputy Counsel, Office of the Chief of Support Services, Department of the Army, Washington, D.C.

McKERN, Thomas W., Ph.D., Professor of Anthropology, University of Kansas, Lawrence, Kan.

Mellon, Joseph, Washington, D.C.

*MUNSTER, Daniel F., Col., USA, Chief of Support Services, Department of the Army, Washington, D.C.

Murray, J. Alden, Ph.D., Natick, Mass.

Nahan, Joseph F., Maj., USA (Ret.), Vienna, Va.

*NEEP, Wesley A., Identification Officer (Human Remains), Army Mortuary, Tan Son Nhut, Vietnam

Newman, Russell W., Ph.D., Natick, Mass.

Owen, Cannon A., Col., MC, USA, Washington, D.C.

Perper, Joshua A., M.D., Baltimore, Md.

Raether, Howard C., P.D., LL.B., Milwaukee, Wis.

Ralston, Robert W., Dayton, Ohio

Reay, Donald T., Maj., MC, USAF, Washington, D.C.

Rhodes, Robert S., Capt., MC, USA, Washington, D.C.

St. Hoyme, Lucile, Ph.D., Washington, D.C.

SALLEY, John J., D.D.S., Ph.D., Dean and Professor of Pathology, University of Maryland School of Dentistry, Baltimore, Md.

Scalise, Joseph L., East Meadow, N.Y.

*Schindler, LeRoy J., Tachikawa, Japan.

Schwaderer, George J., Dayton, Ohio

Sears, Fred R., North Syracuse, N.Y.

Shannon, Dexal R., Maj., USAF, Washington, D.C.

Smith, Paul, Maj., USMC, Washington, D.C.

Snow, Clyde C., Ph.D., Oklahoma City, Okla.

Springate, Charles, M.D., Baltimore, Md.

Stahl, Charles J., Comdr., MC, USN, Washington, D.C.

STEELE, D. Gentry, Graduate Student in Anthropology, University of Kansas, Lawrence, Kan.

STEWART, T. D., M.D., Senior Physical Anthropologist, Department of Anthropology, National Museum of Natural History, Smithsonian Institution, Washington, D.C.

*Tolzmann, Adrian A., Bangkok, Thailand

TROTTER, Lester, LL.M., Assistant Director, Identification Division, Federal Bureau of Investigation, Washington, D.C.

TROTTER, Mildred, Ph.D., Professor Emeritus and Lecturer, Department of Anatomy, Washington University School of Medicine, St. Louis, Mo.

*Wardle, Donald K., Col., USA, Washington, D.C.

Wilson, Edward F., M.D., Baltimore, Md.

Wilson, Robert, Wheaton, Ill.

WITTMUS, Ronald, Fingerprint Technician, Latent Fingerprint Service, Identification Division, Federal Bureau of Investigation, Washington, D.C.

*Witzel, Carl J., Frankfurt, Germany

WOOD, Hobart R., M.D., Medical Examiner, Mecklenburg County, Charlotte, N.C.

Welcome to the Smithsonian

Sidney R. Galler

Colonel Munster, Dr. Stewart, ladies and gentlemen: It is a personal as well as a professional privilege to welcome all of you to the Smithsonian Institution today in behalf of the Board of Regents and the Secretary of the Smithsonian Institution, Mr. S. Dillon Ripley. Basically, I suppose the reason that we are all assembled here in the Smithsonian today to participate in a seminar on Personal Identification in Mass Disasters, is because of the fluke of fate that occurred in the 1840s when the Smithsonian's original benefactor, James Smithson, made the bequest that led to the formation of this organization. He had but one important charge in his bequest; namely, that the monies bequeathed be used for the "increase and diffusion of knowledge among men." If Smithson had not had such a broad vision of science, his institution might not have taken the form that has attracted us here today.

The Smithsonian Institution, as some of you probably are unaware, is not a typical federal agency; depending on which sector of the community you wish to emphasize, it is a quasi-federal or quasi-private establishment chartered by Congress; and, therefore, it is in a rather unique position to facilitate the increase and diffusion of knowledge among men. On the other hand, I'm sure most of you are aware of the Institution as a great complex of museums and public exhibitions; however, some of you may be surprised to know that, historically, the Institution was first a research organization and only subsequently became involved in the keeping of the museums—the public exhibitions and the national collections. Institutionally, I might say, it is the only non-mission oriented, functioning, research laboratory in the descriptive life sciences at the national level, and I think its resulting neutrality stands it in good stead, especially regarding discussions such as the ones that are to be engaged in during these three days. I say this because the Support Services are involved in some of the most sensitive responsibilities in the Army and, I might add parenthetically, in my view the most sensitive responsibilities in the whole of the national establishment.

I suspect that the Support Services might not have asked the Smithsonian to sponsor this seminar had it not been for Dr. T. Dale Stewart's assistance to the Army in matters of identification of personnel over the many years since World War II. Incidentally, Dr. Stewart's connection with the Smithsonian goes back to about 1924, if I am not mistaken, when he became a temporary aide to the late Dr. Aleš Hrdlička, the Smithsonian's first curator of physical anthropology. In 1942 he succeeded Dr. Hrdlička and later became, successively, the head curator of anthropology, and the director of the Museum of Natural History. I might say, again parenthetically, Dr. Stewart's distinguished career as the director of the Museum of Natural History is a phase of his career that I knew during my period with the Office of Naval Research when the Navy called on the Smithsonian Institution for assistance. He is now one of our distinguished senior scientists and, like his predecessor, a member of the National Academy of Sciences, and—forgive me for a little bit of horn-tooting—I think our Institution probably has as many representatives in the National Academy of Sciences as any group at the national level.

I asked Dr. Stewart how long the Army has been consulting him on identification matters. He replied that the earliest contact relating to the present occasion that he could recall was shortly after World War II. The year was 1948, and the work of identifying the war dead from the Pacific theater was already well under way. That year the American Association of Physical Anthropologists held its annual meetings here—in fact in this very building—and included in its program a symposium on "Applied Physical Anthropology." Two of the symposium papers, those by Dr. Stewart and the late Dr. Charles E. Snow, have a place in this historical account. Dr. Stewart drew upon his experience as a consultant with the FBI to talk about "Medico-Legal Aspects of the Skeleton: Age, Sex, Race and Stature." One point that he made in his paper now seems to him particularly significant in view of subsequent developments. He noted that stature estimation from the long bones of the American war dead was still based on the 50 male, 50 female, French cadavers—many of them senile individuals, I should say—measured by Rollet in 1888. Because of this, he stressed the need not only for "better correlation data for Whites, but special data for other races and a better idea of the probable error involved in individual determinations."

Dr. Snow, a physical anthropologist who had just spent six months at the Army Central Identification Laboratory in Hawaii, reported on his experiences there, using the title "The Identification of the Unknown War Dead." For many of those present, this was the first indication of the opportunities afforded by the war dead for the application of anthropological knowledge.

Dr. Stewart remembers that representatives of the Memorial Division, the Office of the Quartermaster-General, attended this symposium. Their main interest was in finding an anthropologist to replace Dr. Snow, who was returning to his teaching post at the University of Kentucky. The person they finally enlisted to continue the identification work in Hawaii was Dr. Mildred Trotter of St. Louis, then professor of gross anatomy at the Washington University School of Medicine. She was present at the symposium 20 years ago and, I might say, the charming Dr. Trotter is here with us today. It is a privilege for me to ask her to stand.

Dr. Stewart thinks that he and Dr. Snow helped persuade Dr. Trotter to accept employment with the Memorial Division, and that he planted the idea in Dr. Trotter's mind of doing something about improving the estimation of stature from long bones. In any case, while in Hawaii during the period 1948-1949, she succeeded, in spite of some substantial administrative obstacles, in proving that it is feasible and, indeed, desirable through research on the war dead to establish a better base for stature estimation. Dr. Trotter's accomplishment, culminating in a superb publication in 1952, set a precedent and, therefore, paved the way in 1954, following the Korean war, for the Memorial Division to invite Dr. Stewart to extend identification research to the dead from another war. This time Dr. Stewart saw the need for better criteria for skeletal aging and persuaded the Memorial Division to let him exert his efforts in this direction. Accordingly, he spent five months during the period 1954–55 at the Army Central Identification Laboratory in Japan on a research project that resulted in a publication in 1957. I am pleased to say that Dr. Thomas W. McKern, who ably assisted in the preparation of that publication, is also here today and I would like Dr. McKern also to stand.

Following his return from Japan in 1955, Dr. Stewart, in association with Dr. Trotter, organized an identification seminar for the Wenner–Gren Foundation of New York. It was held here, again in this building, but the subject was limited to skeletonized remains and to the determinations thereon that particularly concern physical anthropologists. On that occasion, not only were the military services well represented, but some of their identification specialists participated in the panel discussions. One such participant was Mr. C. T. Noll of the Memorial Division, who, incidentally, last spring led the delegation from the Support Services to sound out Dr. Stewart about developing the present seminar. And let me say at this point, I was absolutely delighted that Dr. Stewart and his colleagues in Support Services were able to reach an agreement that led to the formation of the seminar being held here today. I would like to take this moment to ask Mr. Noll to stand and take a bow—much deserved. He is not here? I am so sorry. Well, I would like to take this moment, then, to give him special recognition for his efforts.*

The point I have been documenting in some detail, namely, that the immediate reason you are assembled in the Smithsonian Institution today, as I see it, is because of Dr. Stewart and his interest in personal identification, can be looked at in perhaps another way. Neither the Smithsonian nor Dr. Stewart has any ambition to take over any part of the identification field; indeed, we have enough of a problem identifying the 60 million objects—more or less—that we have in our national collections. We have no mission in this direction or, as I put it earlier, we are non-mission oriented, and our desire is simply to be of service, especially to other sister organizations such as the Support Services of the Army. To reiterate in the words of our principal benefactor, James Smithson, our aim is to increase and diffuse knowledge among men. I think the record, regarding our relationship with the Support Services and with its sister unit, the Memorial Division, bears this out.

I get the impression from the topics to be discussed, and from the affiliations of the faculty as listed, that there are a number of organizations represented here that are connected with federal and state governments. Many of these probably have special interests and missions in the field of personal identification. From my own long experience in government service, I would be surprised if this extraordinarily interesting and complex situation has not resulted in a certain amount of—it says here, "rivalry and conflict of interest," but I prefer to say, "jockeying for position." In any case, I hope the neutrality and the congeniality that the Smithsonian provides for this meeting will prove conducive to frank, friendly, and fruitful discussions.

As I indicated earlier, the Smithsonian provides, besides the neutrality, the organizer of this seminar, Dr. Stewart. As a physical anthropologist with a medical training, Dr. Stewart brings to this role a perspective that is the result of many years of work on skeletal remains of all races, and for many thousands of years of human history. Dr. Lawrence Angel, another distinguished anthropologist of the Smithsonian Institution, and on this occasion Dr. Stewart's deputy, is also here with us today. Dr. Angel would you kindly stand? We have, in the person of Dr. Angel, the third curator in the division's 65 years of existence—a long and honorable tradition indeed. He, too, has had an extensive identification experience, in part from teaching anatomy and studying ancient skeletons, and in part from serving as a consultant to the FBI. And I believe that he continues in those roles. Under the circumstances then, the particular background of these two men has enabled them to work freely with all of the parties concerned in this special area.

Dr. Stewart has been especially concerned to arrange a program that would be most beneficial to the Army Support Services and, indeed, to identification specialists in general. Although this is a large order, it seems to me that the program does offer something for everyone and brings together many people who can profit from this form of communication. I wish you well. You have a very important task ahead of you—a task that in one form or another affects, or has affected, most of us. I hope you have the fullest success in your endeavors at this seminar, and please let us know if we can be of any further assistance to you. Thank you.

---

*Mr. Noll was attending the funeral of Mr. Hugh Munro, Chief, Memorial Affairs Division, Headquarters USAF, who was killed in an automobile accident on the evening of 5 December 1968.—Ed.)

Greetings from the Support Services

Colonel D. F. Munster

Dr. Galler, Dr. Stewart, distinguished scholars, ladies and gentlemen: On behalf of the Department of the Army, and all of the Armed Forces, I am pleased to extend cordial greetings to all of you this morning, and to say how gratified we are that this seminar on Personal Identification in Mass Disasters has materialized.

Because ground troops of the Armed Forces have traditionally borne the brunt of casualties, the Army has a long history of responsibility for the care of American combat dead. Comparatively crude graves registration and identification work began as far back as the Civil War, and it has moved with constantly improving techniques through the Spanish-American War, World Wars I and II, the Korean War, and up to the present. A brief look at the statistics bears out this point.

The Civil War record in identification is bleak indeed. Despite the fact that the conflict took place on American soil between opposing American forces, the care of those who died was left largely to combat commanders rather than to trained specialists. As a result, the unidentified dead exceeded 42 percent of all recovered fatalities. After the Spanish-American War, the first return program was undertaken, during which the remains of 1,222 persons were brought home from Cuba and Puerto Rico. With a trained burial corps available to carry out the work, the unidentified cases dropped to 13.6 percent. In World Wars I and II, graves registration units, skilled in identification procedures, were organized in support of combat operations. As a result of their work and that of the postwar recovery and identification programs, the ratio of unidentified decedents again declined sharply—to less than 4 percent. During the Korean conflict, the Army for the first time was able to evacuate combat dead from the battlefields and to bring remains home without temporary burial overseas. Through the excellent work of graves registration units in the field, and the trained staff at the Central Identification Laboratory in Japan, the unidentified ratio further declined to 2.9 percent of recovered fatalities.

We are once again faced, now in Vietnam, with significant numbers of combat fatalities. Although modern techniques and equipment have resulted in vast improvements in our care-of-the-dead programs—so that remains generally are recovered in Vietnam, prepared in oversea Army mortuaries, and returned to the United States in a matter of days or weeks instead of years—the essential foundation for the success of our efforts remains an imaginative, reliable, and believable program of identification.

In Vietnam, the Army has established two mortuaries with identification responsibilities—one at Tan Son Nhut and the other at Da Nang—where all of the recovered remains of Army, Air Force, Navy, and Marine Corps personnel are prepared for return to their homelands. While we believe that the personnel assigned to these installations are conversant with, and apply reliable scientific techniques to identification, we also feel that this opinion should be tested against the knowledge of disinterested experts. With this in mind, the Army approached Dr. T. Dale Stewart to get his reaction to a seminar of the type on which we are now embarking. His enthusiasm and suggestions encouraged us to obtain the formal consent of Mr. S. Dillon Ripley, Secretary of the Smithsonian Institution, for Dr. Stewart to proceed with all arrangements.

The Army originally expected that the seminar would specifically relate to the identification of combat dead, but this limited concept later was modified to include the problems that arise from mass disasters, and to cover the entire range of specialties that contribute to identification work.

While we are interested in technological innovations that will open new approaches to identification work, we also wish to be assured that the methods now employed by the Army are still the best that are available. We also are mindful of the broader purpose: that a revitalized interest in identification work will encourage research which not only will serve military needs, but will also help civilian authorities faced with mass tragedies.

A quotation attributed to Britain's famous Prime Minister, William E. Gladstone, has guided the men and women who have been responsible for the Army's identification and disposition programs: "Show me the manner in which a nation or a community cares for its dead, and I will measure with mathematical exactness the tender sympathies of its people, their respect for the laws of the land, and their loyalty to high ideals." In this context the Army looks upon the subject we shall be considering together during this seminar—the identification of those who have died serving their country—as one of its most sacred and important missions.

I am grateful that you can give your time to these meetings, and I look forward to meeting you individually during the next few days.

Procedures Used by the U.S. Army to Ensure Proper Identification of the Vietnam War Dead and Their Acceptance by the Next-of-Kin

Wesley A. Neep

Families suffer a tremendous shock when they learn their loved ones have been killed while serving in Vietnam. This shock, coupled with confused reports of jungle fighting and mixed emotions concerning our presence in this strange, faraway land, can cause the next-of-kin to be seriously concerned about the circumstances, the cause of death, and the methods used to identify these casualties.

At the close of 1968, more than 75 percent of all United States personnel killed in Vietnam were being identified by matching their fingerprints with the prints maintained in their military records and by the FBI. Such proof of identity is conclusive for official purposes, but it is not adequate to answer the variety of questions posed by families who are puzzled when receiving "non-viewable" remains, and by those who are not cognizant of the importance of fingerprints.

The Army Mortuary System has a long history of experience in the handling of war casualties, is fully aware of the problem areas in this extremely sensitive mission, and is constantly striving to provide overwhelming evidence to substantiate each identification to the complete satisfaction of all concerned.

In determining war casualty identifications, it is basically understood that only a limited number of deaths occur at any specific location, on a certain date, at a given hour, and under a combination of circumstances pertinent to each individual casualty. These factors are all taken into consideration, along with the more positive means of identification, to present the most complete picture possible concerning each remains.

The identification procedure begins immediately, at the first report of loss or death, by the recovery of the remains in the field. Immediately following each battle, or incident, unit "After Action Reports" provide higher headquarters with data that reflect the name of the casualty, his location by grid coordinates, and the date, hour, and circumstances of death. The remains recovery teams tag each remains by indicating the name provided by the parent unit as well as noting the location, date, hour, and general condition of the remains plus any other available clues. If multiple casualties are recovered from a crash or explosion site, it is mandatory to prepare a sketch that indicates the positions in which each remains is found in relation to the wreckage and the surrounding terrain.

Death certificates that consolidate the recovery data and the cause of death are next prepared at the nearest medical facility. The clothing and pocket contents are examined at a remains collecting point for additional clues as to identity, and efforts are made to obtain signed "Statements of Recognition" by two persons best acquainted with each casualty.

Each remains is thoroughly processed for positive identification at the mortuary prior to release for embalming and airlift home. All clothing is examined and itemized according to type, size, color, name tape, laundry markings, rank, and unit insignia. After cleansing, the fingers are printed (Air Force flying personnel are footprinted), and the body is measured for height and closely scrutinized from all aspects. An anatomical chart (Figure 1) is prepared to define race, height, hair color, mutilated areas, penetrating wounds, abrasions, burned areas, incisions, tatoos, moles, birthmarks, antemortem digital amputations, size and shape of scars, anomalies, healed fractures, and missing body portions. The wounds and general appearance of each remains are then compared with the death certificate statement as to the cause of death. Occasional contradictions are clarified by reexamination, and a doctor prepares a corrected death certificate as required.

All remains not immediately identified by accompanying fingerprint records are given a dental examination. A detailed dental chart (Figure 2), is prepared, which accounts for each tooth with word and graphic descriptions as to extractions, unerupted or impacted teeth, caries, restorations, drifting, interdental spacings, rotations, overlapping, inclinations, alignment, retained deciduous teeth, supernumerary teeth, and the presence of prosthetic appliances.

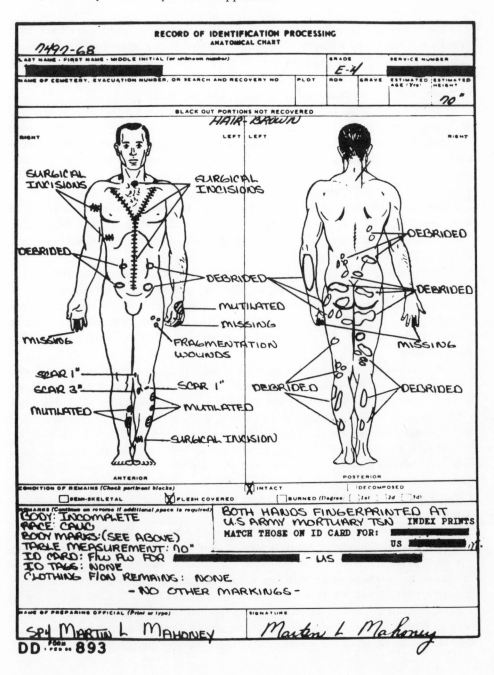

Figure 1. Department of the Army form 893: Record of identification processing—anatomical chart.

The results of identification processing and the associated case papers are then reviewed for content and accuracy. Comparisons are made with fingerprint records and physical/dental data for all involved casualties so that each remains is matched with the record data for the proper individual, and to the exclusion of all others.

Remains recovered from crash and explosion sites are usually more difficult to identify and require more sophisticated examination techniques. By many years of practical experience, the technicians at the Army Mortuary Central Identification Laboratory are highly qualified in the identification of victims lost in military and commercal aircrashes, explosions, fires, highway accidents, earthquakes, floods, shipwreck, and other disasters. They are well trained and proficient in the recognition and interpretation of anatomical and skeletal portions that have been made "unrecognizable and confusing" by mutilation, dismemberment, charring, calcination, decomposition, and intermingling. Portions of commingled remains are segregated according to race, height, weight, morphology, blood type, and the microscopic examination of attached hair strands.

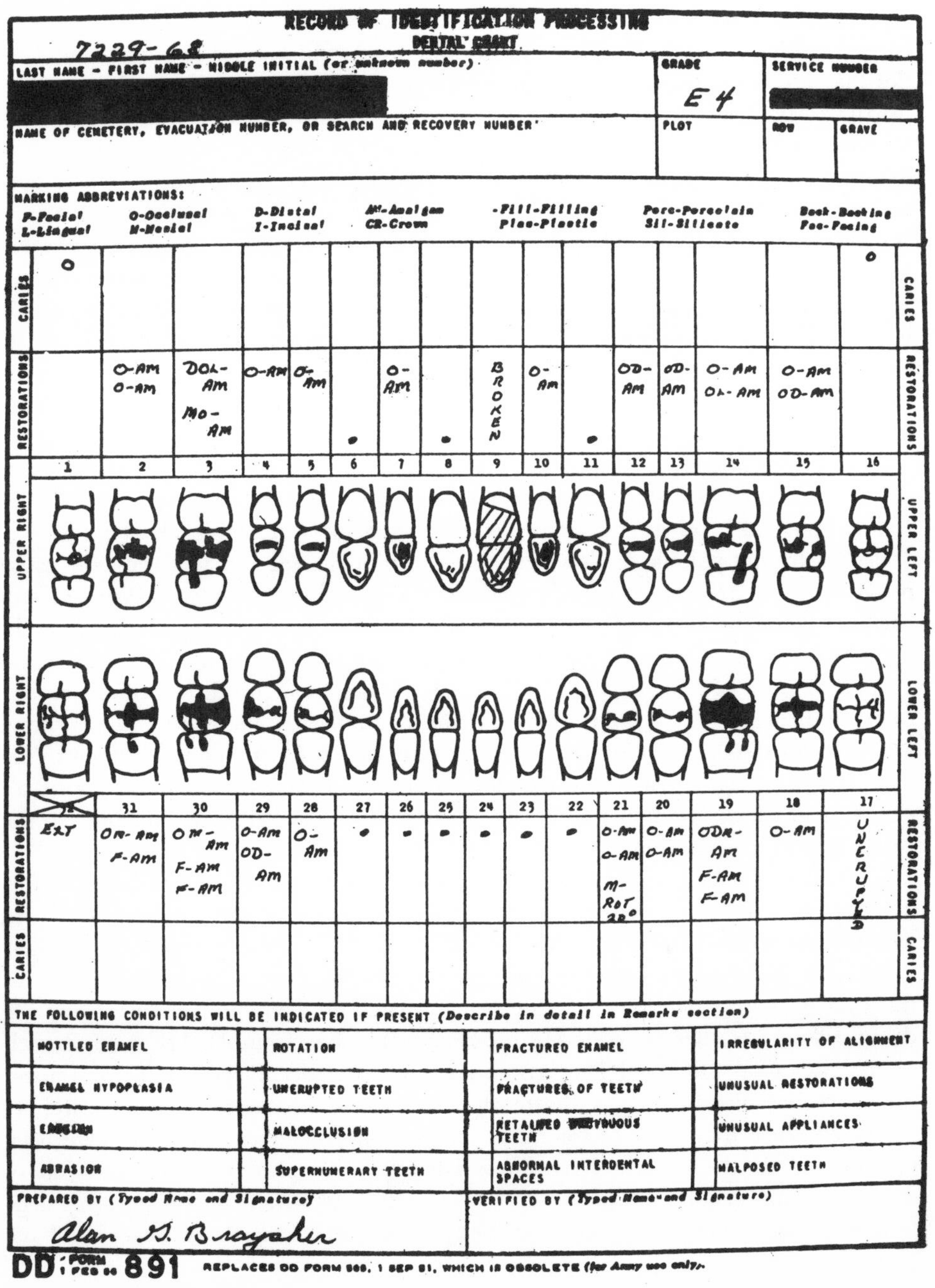

Figure 2. Department of the Army form 891: Record of identification processing—dental chart.

7

The reconstitution of individual remains from mutilated and fragmented portions is accomplished by direct matching and joining of adjacent parts, and by the association of isolated parts according to the recorded characteristics of each victim. The separate identification of dismembered hands and feet, by matching prints, and the association of jaw structures by a match with dental records, make natural starting points in building up each remains. Equally valuable aids are found in identifiable clothing remnants attached, or fused, to remains portions, the presence of tattoos, scars, exceptional growths of hair, and other outstanding body markings.

The X-ray view is widely used to determine and verify internal injuries, to establish age, to verify healed fractures, and to locate surgical pins, screws, and plates. The ultraviolet lamp is used to locate and define tattoos and scars on burned and decomposed remains, in the segregation of skeletal portions, and in the interpretation of illegible ink markings on clothing. When suitable whole blood is not available for testing, then cancellous bone specimens are treated at the special Army Blood Typing Center in Saigon for blood group determination.

On rare occasions there is insufficient recorded information for the determination of a conclusive identity. This applies principally to personnel whose records, being carried at time of death, have been lost or destroyed, and also for nonmilitary casualties that are without benefit of military health and dental records. Such cases can usually be resolved by the technique of matching a life-portrait photograph with a similar one taken of the decedent. The head of the viewable, or skeletal, remains is first photographed from the same angle used for the original portrait, and both comparison photos are then reproduced to equal size. A "negative" or "overlay tracing," prepared from one of the photos, can now be superimposed on the other for direct comparison. All surfaces, contours, orifices, and relative measurements will match if the photos represent one and the same individual. It is especially effective if the subject was smiling and exposing several teeth in the original photo. Enlarged views of these teeth—for comparison as to size, spacings, alignment, beveling, chipping, rotation, overlap, etc.—are very convincing factors to establish identity.

A similar technique is used in the matching of life-X-ray views with those taken of the decedent, with due consideration being given to the innumerable areas of comparison that involve relative size, position, and form of each skeletal part.

Besides having pathologists on duty to perform autopsies and to clarify the cause of death, there are also pathology specialists assigned to the Army "Wound Data Medical Evaluation Team" who examine a considerable number of casualties in order to provide, as required, additional data to aid identification.

A "Statement of Identification" (Figure 3), is prepared for all identifications not based on matching fingerprints. This statement summarizes the circumstances, date, and place of death; the date, recovery location, and the condition of remains; the parent unit association of the remains as a specific casualty; and a review of all matching physical/dental characteristics plus other factors that can contribute to the verification of identification.

Regardless of such overwhelming proof of identity, there will always be those few families who refuse to accept the fact that their husband or son has been killed, or who express serious doubt that the remains returned to them are actually of their loved ones. Some of these families are readily convinced by a telephone review of the case by a representative of the Army Memorial Division in Washington. If doubt still persists, they are visited by qualified technicians from the Technical Branch of the Memorial Division. The remains are once again fingerprinted, and these prints are reverified by the FBI. Postmortem changes in appearance are also carefully explained, since they account for many recognition difficulties that may have been encountered. If the remains have already been buried prior to any expression of doubt, they are disinterred and given the same type of review and fingerprint verification. If the remains are not viewable, the full circumstances of death, and the many factors used to establish identity, are then explained in detail from the complete case file. The vast majority of such inquiries have been resolved to the satisfaction of most families.

Perfection in the recovery and identification of war dead is not only keyed to the best interests of the next-of-kin, but it is an absolute requirement for the complete accountability of all casualties. Constant consideration is devoted to whereabouts, and eventual recovery, of missing personnel who have been reported lost in unknown or inaccessible areas, and those known to have been captured, believed-to-be-captured, missing-without-clues, and those designated as deserters and absent-without-leave.

The recovery and positive identification of each individual thus becomes extremely important in reducing the complexities associated with the recovery and identificaton of all remaining missing personnel, as well as fulfilling the Army's prime responsibility of performing the best possible service to the families of men who have made the supreme sacrifice for their country.

STATEMENT OF IDENTIFICATION
(AR 638-60)

INSTRUCTIONS: 1. Prepare in triplicate and distribute as follows:
  a. Original to CX of Spts S, Attn: Memorial Division.
  b. Copy to Army Command.
  c. Copy retained at preparing installation.
2. This statement will be supplemented by signed copies of appropriate Records of Identification Processing (DD Forms 890 through 894).

7049-68

NAME OF DECEASED (Last, First, Middle)	GRADE	SERVICE NUMBER
▉▉▉▉▉▉▉▉	Pfc E-3	▉▉▉▉▉▉

BRANCH OF SERVICE	ORGANIZATION AND BASE
US ARMY	▉ Co, ▉▉▉ Inf, ▉▉ Inf Div.

DATE OF DEATH	PLACE OF DEATH
▉▉▉▉ 1968	Vicinity of Pleiku, RVN.

CONDITION OF REMAINS (Describe briefly in Remarks).

	RECOGNIZABLE		EVIDENCE OF DECOMPOSITION
X	NOT RECOGNIZABLE	X	MANGLED OR MUTILATED
	COMMINGLED		EVIDENCE OF BURNS

MEANS OF IDENTIFICATION

(Check all appropriate boxes and indicate appropriate inclosures. Specify supporting data in Remarks.)

	IDENTIFICATION TAGS		INCLOSURES
	PERSONAL EFFECTS		DD FORM 890
X	DENTAL COMPARISON	X	DD FORM 891 AND SF 603
X	SKELETAL AND ANATOMICAL COMPARISON	X	DD FORM 892 AND/OR DD FORM 893
	FINGERPRINTS	X	DD FORM 894 for left hand only
	VISUAL RECOGNITION		
X	OTHER (Specify in Remarks)	X	Initials tattooed on L/wrist

REMARKS (If additional space is required, continue on separate sheet)

This remains with right arm and portion of head missing and multiple mutilations and lacerations of head, neck and chest area, was received as Pfc ▉▉▉▉▉ on 2 Nov 68 from the Pleiku area. Pfc ▉▉▉▉▉ was reported killed 2 Nov 68 in the Pleiku area. There were no statements of recognition received for this remains. Verification of identity is based on the following observations:

Race - Caucasian. (Pfc ▉▉▉▉ was Caucasian)

Table measurement - Fingertip to sternum 33 7/8" x 2 = 67 3/4" (Pfc ▉▉▉▉ was 68" tall)

Hair - Brown. (Pfc ▉▉▉▉ had Brown hair)

Tattoo - Initials "T. A." L/wrist. (Pfc ▉▉▉▉ had such a tattoo)

Left hand fingerprinted but record prints for Pfc ▉▉▉▉ are not available this mortuary for comparative purposes.

The tooth chart prepared for this remains is in excellent agreement with the dental records for Pfc ▉▉▉▉.

ID tags - None received.

ID card - None received.

Clothing on remains - Jungle fatigues w/o markings
  - Jungle boots, size 9 - XW w/o markings
  - Black socks and black waist belt w/o markings

TO THE BEST OF MY KNOWLEDGE AND BELIEF, THE STATEMENTS MADE HEREIN ARE CORRECT AND TRUE.

DATE	TYPED NAME, GRADE AND TITLE OF IDENTIFYING OFFICER
8 November 68	Wesley A. Neep GS-13 Anthropology Splst
	SIGNATURE OF IDENTIFYING OFFICER

NAME AND ADDRESS OF INSTALLATION

US ARMY MORTUARY, SAIGON

DA FORM 2773
MAR 65

REPLACES DA FORM 2773, 1 FEB 64 WHICH MAY BE USED.

Figure 3. Department of the Army form 2773: Statement of identification.

Identification Involving Atrocities

A. Keith Mant

In any discussions on mass disasters that occur in times of peace, let us not forget that war is the greatest mass disaster of all. Deaths that result from acts of war pose many special identification problems. Indeed, the instrument responsible for death may be so destructive that it will completely obliterate its victim and render identification, by even the most generous criteria, impossible.

The identification problems about to be discussed concern persons who were buried in the field or behind enemy lines, and who were exhumed some considerable time later. The vast majority of these burials were handled by war graves units. The pathological unit, attached to the War Crimes Group, was put into the field as an independent unit to establish in cases of suspicion whether death was the result of legitimate warfare or of a war crime. It operated in close liaison with the war graves units.

The identification of war-crimes victims by a pathologist was often rendered difficult by the attempts of the enemy to cover up their crimes. This paper describes the various associated problems and how they were tackled during the two and a half years the author was in charge of the special medical section of the British War Crimes Group in northwest Europe immediately following World War II.

During the later stages of the war, a number of allied airmen or special-service troops, after having been taken prisoner, were murdered. These murders were not usually carried out by the Wehrmacht, but rather by the s.s., or by the civilians who were formed into paramilitary units when the Nazis began to retreat. When one considers the eight million who were murdered in the concentration camps, these other murders form a very small proportion of the total German atrocities. The War Crimes Group, beside investigating the major atrocities and bringing the instigators to trial, also investigated the individual murders of service personnel, and the purpose of the medical section was both to ascertain whether a crime had been committed and to establish the identity of the victim, or victims. It was not possible to investigate every allegation, and the medical section usually was briefed only when it appeared that a war crime was involved, and when the names of the perpetrators were known, and they were either in custody or believed to be alive.

In the immediate postwar period, the personnel of the unit consisted of a pathologist, two photographers, one experienced laboratory technician, and five private soldiers who functioned both as drivers and grave diggers. The photographers undertook the photography for the whole of the War Crimes Group. As a result of demobilization in mid-1946, the unit was reduced to a pathologist, one photographer, a junior laboratory technician, and three private soldiers and a secretary-interpreter. The equipment, other than photographic, consisted of a set of postmortem instruments, aprons, gloves, hand-digging equipment, a saloon car, and a 15 cwt. truck. There was a darkroom and another small room for use both as a laboratory and to photograph specimens. I give these details since the available equipment, personnel, and facilities determined the methods and techniques employed.

Any investigation was initially instigated by a request for an exhumation from the intelligence or legal sections.

The brief usually included the name, number and, occasionally, a description of the deceased, although this often came later, along with a narrative of the events surrounding the death. The pathologist was requested to establish the identity of the deceased and, if he was in a mass grave, of all the occupants of the grave. He then was asked to establish the cause of death and to supply considerable information concerning the killing.

Identity was established or confirmed in a variety of ways and, whenever possible, the identity established by one method was cross-checked by other methods.

Every effort was made to establish positively the identification of all British, Commonwealth, and United States war crimes victims. It was not possible, nor ever attempted, to identify individually concentration camp victims who were frequently buried naked in mass graves, but merely to identify a certain person or persons believed to be buried amongst the other victims. The identification was also considered impossible amongst slave workers, often of unknown nationality, who were buried in unmarked graves without any records or means of personal identification. With regard to air casualties, at the time of exhumation every attempt was made to establish the identity of the deceased or, if this were not possible, to hand over to a graves registration unit sufficient data to allow a positive identification from records.

Badly Mutilated Bodies in Mass Graves

On a few occasions the special medical section examined what amounted to several bundles of bones, with or without flesh attached. These bundles represented the remains of the crew of an aircraft that had crashed, caught alight, and exploded. Sometimes no fragments were larger than a few inches. In this type of problem, the scope of the pathologist and the anatomist was severely limited. Two questions arose: what was the plane and how many dead were represented in the bundles of remains? Concerning the first question, the fragments of clothing had to be carefully examined for a name or service number, or even the presence of an identity tag. The identification of one member of the crew would enable the aircraft to be identified, and thus the number of persons missing from the aircraft could be ascertained from records.

With respect to actual identification of the various bodies, this was often a long and tedious exercise. It usually was essential to clean the bony fragments before they could be adequately examined. In practice, it was found that the most reliable method of counting the bodies was to count the femoral heads. Subcapital fractures were common and the head remaining in the acetabulum, in spite of fire, was usually well preserved. These femoral heads were collected, paired, and counted.

With regard to allocating the bony fragments to specific bodies, this was impossible. It was sometimes possible to allocate several pieces to a particular body, but the pile of unallocated fragments was always large. This raises the question whether it is desirable to try and separate the fragments once the plane is identified and the names of dead aircrew known. In those cases where the apportioning of bony fragments to a particular body is impossible or impractical it is logical to bury the remains in a single grave with the names on a common headstone.

A very high rate of identification is possible in the field without the application of sophisticated techniques. When the investigator is in possession of the physical data of the deceased at the time of his examination, positive identification should be certain, but even without prior knowledge of identity, positive identification is usually achieved by examination of clothing, pocket contents, and local records.

Table I shows the numbers of actual war-crimes cases exhumed by the medical section, and the numbers which were positively identified. It will be seen that only two apparently British victims were unidentified out of a total of 42 British, Commonwealth, and United States service personnel.

TABLE I
Success in Identifying War Crimes Cases

	British	U.S.	Others
Total	35	7	18
Positive identification	33	6	2
Sufficient data to establish identity	—	1	2
Unidentified	2 (?)	—	14

Table II shows the numbers of air casualties and that out of a total of 38, three were unidentified. These three were all from the same plane; the largest skeletal remains was no more than six inches long; therefore, it was not possible to allocate the portions of bone to each body. The fourth member of the crew was also badly injured, but had sufficient clothing to enable his fragmented remains, and hence the aircraft, to be identified.

TABLE II
Success in Identifying Air Casualties*

	British	U.S.	Others
Total	35	1	2
Positively identified	26	1	2
Sufficient data to establish identity	6	—	—
Unidentified	3	—	—

* Identifications by autopsy on behalf of graves units are not included.

Table III shows the means by which identifications were established, and it is the methods that were used which make up the substance of this paper. The table merely shows what was considered the most reliable means of identification in any one case; it does not include all the cross-checking that was carried out. For example, if a man was identified from his clothing, his physical characteristics would be checked with his records when these were available. Pocket contents that confirmed identification were frequently found, but these were considered unreliable for positive identification. It is of interest to note that, of the 39 British and United States war crimes cases, only eight were identified by their clothing while, of the 26 aircraft victims, 19 were identified by their clothing.

TABLE III
Methods of Identification in War Crimes and Air Casualties

Method of Identification	WAR CRIMES			AIR CASUALTIES		
	British	U.S.	Allied	British	U.S.	Allied
Graves unit plus autopsy	6	5	—	7	—	—
Cemetery records alone	2	—	—	—	—	2
Cemetery records plus autopsy	6	—	2	—	—	—
Identity discs	4	—	—	—	1	—
Dental data	4	—	—	—	—	—
Clothing	7	1	—	19	—	—
Service watch	1	—	—	—	—	—
Signet ring	1	—	—	—	—	—
Tattoo	1	—	—	—	—	—
Pocket contents	1	—	—	—	—	—
Totals identified:	33	6	2	26	1	2

Before discussing the methods of identification, something should be said about the special problems associated with the identification of persons who had died as the result of a war crime. Many of the victims were airmen who had bailed out of their planes. After having been taken prisoner, they were taken out and shot, usually through the back of the head or neck—the *Genickschuss*. The disposal of the body, or bodies, varied. The war-crimes victims might be placed in a mass grave with the rest of the crew, they might be buried in an unmarked grave in a cemetery, or buried near where they were shot. Occasionally, they were buried in a cemetery and a cross was erected. Means of identification, such as identity discs, were usually removed, pockets were emptied, and uniforms were removed or stripped of all insignia—indeed sometimes all articles of clothing were removed from the deceased. Sometimes they would be buried in a media that accelerated decomposition. With air-crash victims, the clothing search was more superficial, and although identity discs were often removed, the clothing was usually left intact. Burial normally took place in a cemetery, and the names, ranks, and service numbers of the dead were recorded in the cemetery records. Usually a cross, or crosses, were erected and given the names of the persons in the grave.

Eleven cases of war crimes had previously been exhumed by British or United States graves units, and these units were satisfied with their identification. The United States graves units sometimes used the services of the British War Crimes medical section when they were in the British Zone of Germany and found any evidence to suggest that the servicemen they had exhumed had unusual gunshot wounds. The British cases that were identified by the graves units were exhumed in East Germany. The medical section was never given permission to travel into the Russian Zone and so was unable to be present at an exhumation.

The respective graves units were often supplied with the physical details of the men they exhumed and, as a result, the medical section was able to compare the dental and physical data of each deceased with his records to confirm identification. In one case, the medical section discovered that two bodies brought from the Russian Zone of Germany had been switched in transit.

In only two British cases exhumed by the medical section was it necessary to rely on cemetery records. In peacetime, one would never expect cemetery records to be in error. In war, mistakes might be anticipated, and difficulties occasionally arose where the perpetrators of the crimes had ordered the cemetery keepers to bury their victims in unrecorded graves, or even under false names.

German cemetery keepers, however, did not lack in teutonic efficiency and meticulous observance of detail, so although the official cemetery records might have been falsified, the cemetery keeper had his own records, which were accurate. In one case, where two Polish airmen had been buried under false names, their true names had been written inside their coffin lids!

It was a comparison of the physical and dental data in the records, with those of the deceased, that provided an opportunity to study the actual efficiency and reliability of the methods that are taught in any routine course in forensic medicine. I shall go through these methods in some detail, emphasizing any lessons learned.

Estimation of Stature

When the physical data of the deceased was supplied, the height was invariably included and, in all cases, whether or not physical data was available, an estimation of the height was made. Depending upon the state of the body, two methods were employed. In the immediate postwar period, the bodies were usually intact. War-crimes victims, although frequently buried without coffins, were laid out in the grave and, after the body had been carefully uncovered, a measurement would be made before it was lifted. Later, when the bodies were very decomposed, and one was dealing with little more than skeletal remains, or when decomposed bodies, which had been removed by graves units, arrived for examination in a disintegrated state, measurements of the long bones were made, and the heights calculated by the application of Pearson's formula. The estimations were usually a little below that of the recorded height but, as in most cases, positive identification was established in other ways, and the difference between the estimated and recorded heights was not considered to invalidate the identification. In all cases where it was possible to measure four long bones, and the estimated heights from each individual bone was close, the average of the four bones gave an estimated height within ± 1 inch of the recorded height. If there were significant variations, then the final average was often unreliable. Direct measurements of the intact body sometimes showed discrepancies, which suggested that some of the original records were inaccurate.

Most of these estimations were carried out in the field. The majority of the original notes have now been destroyed, but of the ones retained, it has since been possible to reestimate the height by the use of the formula of Trotter and Gleser. Estimations of stature using this more recent formula have been remarkably accurate.

Sexing

This was never a problem. Only two women, both parachutists who had been shot at contact range through the backs of their necks, were exhumed in this series, and both of these women were exceptionally well preserved.

Color of Eyes

This characteristic was of no value in this series.

Hair

A description of the length, color, and waviness of the hair offered useful contributory evidence in identification. Samples were taken from each body and then dried before final examination.

Fingerprints

Fingerprints were not available for comparison.

Tattoos

One war-crime victim had his Christian name tattooed upon his forearm, and this was clearly recognizable.

Dental Data

Theoretically, a comparison of the deceased's dentition with his dental records should provide positive identification. In many cases, the dental records received were inaccurately completed, or not kept up to date and, as this means of identification depends entirely upon the accuracy and completeness of the records, the results were often disappointing.

Dental data was recorded in every case, either by filling in a dental chart and photographing the teeth, or by excising the upper and lower jaws and comparing them with the dental records, if and when they became available at a later date.

To illustrate how misleading incorrect dental data could be when one is confronted with a large number of bodies, there was a case where eight bodies were buried in a single grave. The names of the eight men were known, and it was merely a matter of identifying each individual. The actual case concerned a stick of eight s.a.s. personnel who had been captured, and who were then taken out to a forest, where they were made to dig a grave, after which they were executed. The Germans attempted to remove all means of identification, and the grave was filled in and left unmarked. It was known that the attempt had been made to remove all means of identification, and so the medical section was provided with identity photographs of all eight victims, and the dental data of seven. Of the seven dental charts supplied, only three were accurate. Two were inaccurate but, in conjunction with the full examination, sufficiently adequate to identify. In fact, one of these victims had two dental records, one showing a full set of teeth, the other showing him to be edentulous: neither was correct; he had one tooth! Finally, there were two remaining bodies, and it was impossible to match the dental records with either to provide an identification, even though there were two names and two bodies. Identification was achieved by building up a description of each man—height, color and length of hair, build, etc.—and then contacting a member of the same unit who was able to identify the two immediately. It is of interest that, in spite of attempts to remove all means of identification, one pocket in the officer's shirt had not been searched, a watch had been missed on a soldier's wrist, and a signet ring had not been removed from another. How identification of each victim was achieved is shown in Table IV.

TABLE IV

Identification of Eight Murdered S.A.S. Personnel*

Body no.	Dental data	Other means
1	Not available	Photograph. Pocket contents, including a personal letter.
2	Accurate	
3	Accurate	
4	Accurate	Tattoo on forearm
5	Inaccurate, but adequate	Signet ring
6	Inaccurate, but adequate	Number on Service watch
7	Inaccurate	Recognized by colleague from physical description supplied from exhumation findings such as height, build, features, color and length of hair.
8	Inaccurate	

* The methods of identification listed were all supplemented by the physical data obtained at exhumation, and these data were compared with each man's personal records.

In actual war-crimes cases, photographs were of more value than might be expected, because the victims were buried immediately after having been shot and sometimes buried in a deep grave. Rapid earth burial, without a coffin, and especially if the grave is deep, retards decomposition and, hence, in the cases exhumed shortly after the end of hostilities, the features were often well-preserved.

An examination of clothing was usually rewarding, even when it was distintegrating as a result of burial in wet soil. The handling of the clothing was largely one of commonsense. Where the clothing was so friable that any attempt to remove it whole would result in its distintegration, it was removed in panels, with special care being taken while removing panels that were usually marked with the decedent's name and number. Clothing in good condition was washed and scrubbed at the graveside. Distintegrating clothing was laid out and carefully dried and later gently scraped and sponged.

From the clothing examined, names and numbers were almost invariably developed by these methods. Not infrequently, in the case of officers, two sets of numbers were developed, the one held before commission and the commissioned number.

The service number, with or without the name or initials, was most frequently developed from the neckband of the shirt.

It is interesting to note that the United States metal identity disc was superior to the composition disc of the British. The British discs sometimes became distorted, and even partly disintegrated, after a period in a grave, and this necessitated a laboratory examination in order to establish identity. Why the discs should disintegrate in a grave, has never been discovered. They have been boiled in the laboratory continuously for a week without any significant damage occurring, even after the addition of caustic alkalis or mineral acids to the solution.

The investigation of alleged war crimes, and the identification of the victims, was a product of the last war and, when the investigations were first initiated, it was not appreciated how many problems would arise. If one had known in 1945 what was known by 1946, when the army was being demobilized, it would have been possible to put several pathological units into the field.

With regard to equipment, a mobile X-ray unit would have been useful, especially for localizing bullets and other metallic objects, but the need for sophisticated laboratory tests was rare. Any material that required special examination could easily be sent to a base laboratory.

As for personnel, the most important consideration is to select and train a unit capable of undertaking specialist work, one that can receive instruction and that can understand precisely what the operation is all about. A properly trained field unit is worth more than all of the expensive equipment and organization at the base, for the mistakes made at exhumation are unlikely to be corrected later. And, of course, the officer in charge of the squad, even when exhumation is for the purpose of identification only, should have a sound basic training, which must include a working knowledge of anatomy, and he must be able to utilize the services and personnel at his disposal to the best advantage.

In conclusion, it should be emphasized that the identification of war casualties, as with the identification of casualties following any peacetime mass disaster, can be efficiently and accurately accomplished provided the persons who first handle the bodies know their job. Naturally, different situations will require individual assessment and treatment and this, of course, will depend upon the ingenuity of the person in charge of operations.

Cytologic Sexing

Howard S. Grob

The discovery of sexual dimorphism in the neurons from the spinal cord of cats (Barr and Bertram, 1949) led to subsequent studies that have demonstrated a cytological sex marker in a wide variety of body tissues, and in a great number of mammalian species, including the human (Moore and Barr, 1954; Moore, 1966b). The sex marker (sex chromatin mass) is a nuclear structure that can be seen in many types of somatic cells by histologic examination of the preserved tissues. It is seen, normally, only in cells from females.

Morphologic Characteristics

The sex chromatin is a discrete mass of nuclear chromatin that is in apposition to the inner surface of the nuclear membrane. The mass is generally planoconvex in shape. Its average dimensions are about 0.8×1.1 micra, with a range of 0.7×1.0 to 1.0×1.4 micra. In fixed and stained preparations, the mass takes the nuclear dye with great avidity; it is both hyperchromatic and hyperpyknotic.

Sex chromatin is both Feulgen positive and destroyed by treatment with deoxyribonuclease, hence it is thought to be in the nature of genetic material. Ohno (1966) has presented convincing evidence for believing that the sex chromatin mass is a biochemically inactive X-chromosome.

The morphological characteristics of the sex chromatin are admirably reviewed in detail by Klinger (1966).

A sex marker, comparable to the sex chromatin, has been described in granulocytic leukocytes (Davidson and Smith, 1954; Davidson, 1966). In well-made smears of peripheral blood from normal females, "drumstick-like" appendages are present. The drumstick is an hyperchromatic, hyperpyknotic mass of nuclear chromatin that has an oval head with an average diameter of 1.0 to 1.5 micra, and that is attached to the nucleus by a thin strand of chromatin material. Like the sex chromatin mass of other cells, the drumstick is Feulgen positive and susceptible to treatment with deoxyribonuclease.

Other nuclear appendages of the leukocyte, which have no known bearing on cytologic sex, may be mistaken for drumsticks by an inexperienced observer.

Distribution and Frequency

Sex chromatin can be visualized in all cell types from the human female, with the exception of those cells which have pyknotic nuclei or heavily condensed nucleoplasm (lymphocytes, hepatic parenchyma, etc.). Nuclei from cells of the basal layers of epidermis, smooth muscle, cartilage, oral epithelium, and the zona fasciculata of the adrenal cortex are particularly suitable for the investigation of cytologic sex (Moore, 1966b).

Reports on the frequency of sex chromatin vary for each tissue under study. These variations may be due both to tissue differences and to a variety of technical factors (Klinger, 1966). Fixation, processing, sectioning, and staining procedures may all affect the frequency with which one observes the sex chromatin in a given tissue. These technical factors will shortly be discussed in greater detail.

In the early literature, the sex chromatin was reported present in low frequency (0–5 percent) in cells from normal human males. These claims, however, have not been substantiated. The general consensus among workers in this field is that the sex chromatin mass is not present in the cells of normal males (Moore, 1966b; Grob and Kupperman, 1961).

There are instances of confirmed discrepancies between the cytologic and phenotypic sex of certain individuals. These generally fall into three major classes:

1. Females that are chromatin negative (sex chromatin mass is absent)
2. Males that are chromatin positive (sex chromatin mass is present)
3. Genetic mosaics in which some tissues are chromatin positive while others are chromatin negative.

Phenotypic females who are chromatin negative are of two types:

1. Some females show the clinical stigmata of Turner's Syndrome (ovarian agenesis). These individuals are generally of short stature, they exhibit primary amenorrhea, absence of secondary sex characteristics and, in many cases, a variety of congenital malformations such as neck webbing, *cubitus valgus*, and coarctation of the aorta. In these patients, karyotypic analysis reveals an abnormal chromosome number, 45 rather than 46, with the absence of one X-chromosome. It is believed that the absence of one X-chromosome is the factor responsible for the negative chromatin pattern.
2. Some females exhibit the stigmata of the syndrome of testicular feminization. These individuals are phenotypic females, but examination of the reproductive tract often reveals labial or inguinal gonads, which are testicular histologically, and the absence of a uterus and oviducts. In these patients, the somatic tissues are thought to be responsive to endogenous estrogens, but not to androgens. Hence there often is adequate breast development, but little or no pubic and axillary hair. Karyotypic analyses of these individuals reveal the normal chromosome number of 46, with the sex chromosome complement being XY.

Phenotypic males who are chromatin positive comprise approximately one half of the total number of cases in which the diagnosis of Klinefelter's Syndrome (primary testicular dysgenesis) has been made. These males have atrophic testes that do not produce spermatozoa. They are characterized by a lack of secondary sex development and often show true gynecomastia. Karyotypic analyses reveal these individuals possess an extra chromosome (47 rather than 46). The idiogram shows three sex chromosomes, which give the patients a genotype of XXY.

Genetic mosaics may be of either phenotypic sex, but their somatic tissues exhibit two or more genotypes. If the genotypic differences are due to changes in the number of X-chromosomes, these may be reflected as differences in the chromatin sex patterns of various tissues taken from a single individual.

Although substantive data are lacking with regard to the frequency of these anomalies, it appears that the total number of individuals who exhibit all of the above noted abberations comprise less than one percent of the general population.

Tissue Processing

Since the determination of cytologic sex is dependent upon the visualization of the sex-chromatin mass, tissue preparations of the highest technical quality are required.

Fixation should be carried out for 24 hours, and using a fixative that preserves nuclear detail. Experience shows a modification of Davidson's fixative gives good results. The formula used is as follows:

Formalin (40% Formaldehyde)	20%
Glacial Acetic Acid	10%
95% Ethanol	35%
Distilled Water	35%

After fixation in this fluid, the tissue blocks are transferred through two changes of 70 percent ethanol over a period of 24 to 48 hours. If storage is necessary, the tissues may be retained for long periods in 70 percent ethanol.

Subsequent to fixation, the tissues should be dehydrated in an ethanol series, then cleared in several changes of xylene, and finally infiltrated and embedded in a matrix for sectioning. Any of the usual paraffin preparations are satisfactory matrices. Recommended, however, is the use of "Paraplast," a paraffin-plastic polymer mixture that reduces infiltration time and provides superior sectioning qualities. The tissues may then be sectioned at a thickness of 5 micra, the sections fixed to slides, and prepared for staining.

Since the sex-chromatin mass is composed of nuclear chromatin material, basophilic dyes are most frequently used for its demonstration. Any of the routine tissue stains may be used (Hematoxylin and Eosin, Feulgen, Cresyl Echt Violet, Papanicolaou, etc.). A more specific stain for the sex-chromatin mass has been developed by Klinger and Ludwig (1957). Their technique exploits the fact that the sex chromatin is more resistant to acid hydrolysis than most other nuclear structures. In this method, the sections are hydrolyzed with HCl and subsequently stained with Thionin. Upon examination, most of the chromatin strands have been removed by the acid treatment, but the nuclear membrane, and the sex-chromatin mass if present, will be stained along with a minor amount of other nuclear materials.

The Test

In practice, the test is performed on slides that carry only an identifying number, so that the individual reading the preparation is not cognizant of the name, sex, or other identifying characteristics of the subject. The slides are prepared by an individual who will not do the reading. The use of such a "double-blind" technique is an aid to allow the investigator to retain objectivity while assigning the cytologic sex for any given preparation.

In reading the tissue sections, only vesicular nuclei are counted, and damaged and pyknotic nuclei are disregarded since artifacts in such nuclei may lead to false positive readings. The presence of definitive sex-chromatin masses, in any frequency whatsoever, indicates the tissue under examination to be chromatin positive. The absence of sex-chromatin masses in good tissue preparations, where adequate numbers of nuclei have been examined, indicates the tissue to be chromatin negative. The question of how many nuclei should be examined before assigning the chromatin-negative result is one for which there is no rigid formula. In our experience, the examination of 300 to 500 nuclei, in which no chromatin-sex masses or suspicious structures are seen, suffices to assign a chromatin-negative result.

It should be emphasized that reliable performance of the test requires a high degree of experience on the part of the observer. Experience with the method may be garnered by performing the test, using the double-blind technique, with tissues taken at autopsy from individuals whose medical history is known. This permits the inexperienced investigator to perform the test and, subsequently, to compare his results with that which is known about the individual from whom the tissue was taken.

Medicolegal Aspects

The medicolegal implications of cytological sexing, including the forensic applications of the test, have been reviewed most recently by Moore (1966a).

Within certain limits, the sex-chromatin test may be a helpful aid when identifying an individual's sex from tissue fragments or mutilated remains. The factors that limit the utility of the test in this regard include the experience of the observer and the degree of autolytic changes which have occurred after death, most importantly the ability of the sex-chromatin mass to take the stain used for its demonstration.

The autolytic changes that occur after death are of little consequence in freshly fixed materials. They may, however, introduce cytomorphological changes in tissues that have not been so treated. Depending upon the surrounding environment, the sex chromatin has been reported to be recognizable in unfixed tissues for periods up to four weeks after death (Dixon and Torr, 1956). In general, in unfixed tissues which have been kept in cool, humidified environments, the sex chromatin is visible in most tissues from chromatin-positive individuals for periods up to approximately one to two weeks after death. Low temperatures and moisture tend to favor the preservation of sex chromatin morphology. It should be noted that tissue autolysis from chromatin-positive individuals can induce the loss of visibility of the sex-chromatin mass. Such a situation might cause a false negative report to be made. It is, therefore, important to qualify this discussion with the statement that autolytically altered tissues may not be reliable indicators of cytologic sex.

A methodology for the detection of sex chromatin from the root sheath cells of human capital hair has recently been reported (Schmid, 1967; Culbertson et al., 1969). The ability of these cell types to resist autolytic changes may render them useful to determine cytologic sex in unfixed remains. In that the hair is stained and sectioned without fixation, processing, or paraffin embedding, the techniques involved in demonstrating sex chromatin in these cells also require less laboratory equipment; in addition, the sections may be made with a scalpel, which obviates the need for microtomy (Culbertson et al., 1969).

The assignment of sex via tissue fragments, particularly from mutilated and scattered remains, must be made with the utmost caution. The possible existence of the various sexual anomalies (Turner's syndrome, Klinefelter's syndrome, etc.), as well as the other factors mentioned above, must be taken into account. When all such factors are weighed carefully, the chromatin-sex technique may then be useful in the identification of human materials.

Literature Cited

Barr, M. L., and Bertram, E. G.
  1949. A morphological Distinction Between Neurones of the Male and Female and the Behaviour of the Nucleolar Satellite During Accelerated Nuclear Protein Synthesis. *Nature* (London), 163: 676-7.
Culbertson, J. C.; Breslau, N. A.; Moore, M. K.; and Engel, E.
  1969. Sex Chromatin Determination from Hair. *Journal of the American Medical Association*, 207: 560-1.
Davidson, W. M.
  1966. Sexual Dimorphism in Nuclei of Polymorphonuclear Leukocytes. In *The Sex Chromatin*, K. L. Moore, editor, W. B. Saunders Co.
Davidson, W. M., and Smith, D. R.
  1954. A Morphological Sex Difference in the Polymorphonuclear Neutrophil Leukocytes. *British Medical Journal*, 2: 6-7.
Dixon, A. D., and Torr, J. B. D.
  1956. Post-mortem Persistence of Sex Chromatin. *Journal of Forensic Medicine*, 3: 161-8.
Grob, H. S., and Kupperman, H. S.
  1961. Experiences With Techniques of Chromatin Sex Determination. *American Journal of Clinical Pathology*, 36: 132-8.
Klinger, H. P.
  1966. Morphological Characteristics of the Sex Chromatin. In *The Sex Chromatin*, K. L. Moore, editor, W. B. Saunders Co.
Klinger, H. P., and Ludwig, K. S.
  1957. A Universal Stain for the Sex Chromatin Body. *Stain Technology*, 32: 235-
Moore, K. L.
  1966a. Sex Chromatin and Medicolegal Problems. In *The Sex Chromatin*, K. L. Moore, editor. W. B. Saunders Co.
  1966b. Sex Chromatin Patterns in Various Animals. In *The Sex Chromatin*, K. L. Moore, editor, W. B. Saunders Co.
Moore, K. L., and Barr, M. L.
  1954. Nuclear Morphology According to Sex, in Human Tissues. *Acta Anatomica*, 21: 197-208.

Ohno, S.
1966.   Single-X Derivation of Sex Chromatin. In *The Sex Chromatin*, K. L. Moore, editor. W. B. Saunders Co.

Schmid, W.
1967.   Sex Chromatin in Hair Roots. *Cytogenetics,* 6: 342-9.

Forensic Neutron Activation Analysis

Vincent P. Guinn

In recent years, the highly sensitive method of high-flux neutron activation analysis (NAA) has found steadily increasing use in the field of scientific crime investigation; i.e., the field of criminalistics. As yet, this technique has not been applied in the field covered by this seminar on personal identification in mass disasters, but it also possesses some possibilities for useful application in this field. In the sections below, the NAA method is briefly described, some of its forensic applications to date summarized, and its potential applications in the field of mass disasters discussed.

The NAA Method

Neutron activation analysis may be very simply defined as a nuclear method of qualitative and quantitative elemental analysis. It typically involves:

1. Placing a small specimen of the material to be analyzed in an irradiation container, usually a small polyethylene vial
2. Exposing the sample to a high flux of thermal neutrons, usually in a research-type nuclear reactor
3. Measuring either instrumentally or, after post-irradiation radiochemical separations with carriers, the various amounts of the now radioactive elements of interest, and which are detectable in the activated sample
4. Calculating the amount and concentration of each detected element of interest in the original sample.

The basic equation of NAA is a simple one:

$$A_o = N \, \emptyset \, \sigma \, S, \tag{1}$$

where:

A_o is the radioactivity level of a particular induced radionuclide, expressed in disintegrations per second (dps), just at the end of an irradiation period, t_i

N is the number of target nuclei in the sample that can form, by a (n, γ) nuclear reaction, the particular radionuclide

$\emptyset$ is the thermal-neutron flux to which the sample was exposed, expressed in units of thermal neutrons per square centimeter per second (n/cm^2-sec)

σ is the isotopic thermal-neutron (n, γ) cross section of the target stable nuclide, expressed in units of square centimeters per nucleus

S is the "saturation factor," a dimensionless quantity that ranges in magnitude from 0 to 1, the exact value depending upon the irradiation period (t_i), and the half-life of the induced activity (T).

The saturation term, S, is determined by the equation:

$$S = 1 - e^{-0.693 \, t_i/T} \tag{2}$$

and acquires values of $\frac{1}{2}$, $\frac{3}{4}$, $\frac{7}{8}$, $\frac{15}{16}$, . . . at the t_i/T values of, respectively, 1, 2, 3, 4. . . . It asymptotically approaches the limiting value of 1 as t_i/T becomes very large.

The term, N, in Equation (1) is related to the desired quantity, w, the weight of the particular element in the sample (in grams), by the equation:

$$N = w \cdot a \cdot N_A / AW \qquad (3)$$

where:

a   is the fractional isotopic abundance, of the particular stable nuclide, amongst the various stable nuclides of the element

N_A is Avogadro's number (6.023×10^{23} atoms per gram-atom)

AW is the chemical atomic weight of the element.

Equations (1), (2), and (3) apply to each (n, γ) radioactive product (radio-nuclide) that is formed in the sample from each element present. In practice, one does not use these equations per se, but instead uses a comparator technique in which known weights of the various elements of interest are activated and counted in exactly the same way as the unknown sample(s). Use of the comparator technique eliminates the need to know the magnitudes of the terms, Θ, σ, S (and hence, t_i), a, N_A, and AW. The resulting, much simpler, equation is then:

$$A_o \text{ (sample)} / A_o \text{ (standard)} = w \text{ (sample)} / w \text{ (standard)}. \qquad (4)$$

Since sample and standard are counted at exactly the same efficiency, the disintegration rates (A_o) can be replaced by the corresponding, experimentally measured, radionuclide counting rates (A'_o):

$$A'_o \text{(sample)} / A'_o \text{(standard)} = w \text{(sample)} / w \text{(standard)}. \qquad (5)$$

Use of Equation (5) eliminates the need to know the exact radioactive decay scheme of the radionuclide, and the counting efficiency. Since each radioactive species decays according to the equation:

$$A_t = A_o e^{-0.693 t/T} \qquad (6)$$

where t is the decay period since t_o—(and T is again the half life of the radionuclide species)—Equation (5) is also valid at any designated decay time; i.e.,

$$A'_t \text{(sample)} / A'_t \text{(standard)} = w \text{(sample)} / w \text{(standard)}. \qquad (7)$$

Equation (7) is the equation used in practice. Since samples and standards are usually measured at different decay times, before insertion into Equation (7) each radionuclide activity is first corrected to what it would be at some particular selected decay time, t, via Equation (6).

In order to obtain some idea of the high sensitivity of the method when high thermal-neutron fluxes are employed, a specific example is of value. Suppose that one wishes to estimate the limit of detection possible for the element *copper* when it is exposed to a typical thermal-neutron flux in a modern one-megawatt (1 Mw) research-type nuclear reactor—10^{13} n/cm²-sec—for one hour. From a chart of the nuclides, (Goldman and Stehn, n.d.), one finds that ordinary copper consists of two stable isotopes (nuclides): ^{63}Cu and ^{65}Cu, which consist, in nature, of 69.09 atom % ^{63}Cu and 30.91 atom % ^{65}Cu. Each of these is capable of capturing a thermal neutron and forming, respectively, 12.80-hour ^{64}Cu and 5.10-minute ^{66}Cu. From the chart, their respective isotopic (n, γ) thermal-neutron capture cross sections are seen to be 4.51 barns and 1.8 barns (one barn = 10^{-24} cm²/nucleus). Copper can be detected by means of either of these induced activities (^{64}Cu or ^{66}Cu), but attention will be restricted here to the ^{64}Cu product. The chemical atomic weight of copper is 63.54.

From Equations (1) to (3), one may calculate that one microgram (1 μg) of copper, after exposure for one hour to a thermal-neutron flux of 10^{13} n/cm²-sec, should generate an initial ^{64}Cu activity, A_o (in dps), of:

$$A_o = [10^{-6} \times 0.6909 \times 6.023 \times 10^{23} / 63.54][10^{13}][4.51 \times 10^{-24}][1 - e^{-0.693 \times 1/12.80}]$$

or

$$1.54 \times 10^4 \text{ dps}.$$

In order to estimate the photopeak counting rate that this amount of ^{64}Cu would produce under the usual counting conditions (2 cm from a 3-inch x 3-inch NaI(Tl) crystal scintillation counter that is coupled to a multichannel pulse-height analyzer), one needs to know the decay scheme of ^{64}Cu and the NaI(Tl) photopeak counting efficiency for the principal gamma ray of ^{64}Cu. From the Table of Isotopes (Lederer et al., 1967), one finds that ^{64}Cu decays by positron emission (β^+) in 19% of its disintegrations. Each of these positrons is annihilated by interaction with an electron (e^-) to produce two 0.511 Mev (0.511 million electron volt) gamma-ray photons that are emitted in opposite directions. From the Gamma-Ray Spectrum Catalogue (Heath, 1964), one finds that the detection efficiency of a 3 x 3 NaI(Tl) detector, at a sample distance of 2 cm, is 0.155 (i.e., 15.5%), and that the fraction of counter pulses in the 0.511 Mev total-absorption peak (photopeak) is 0.625. Thus, a 1.54 x 10^4 dps ^{64}Cu activity would produce a 0.511 Mev photopeak counting rate (cps = counts per second, cpm = counts per minute) of:

1.54 x 10^4 x 0.19 x 0.155 x 0.625 cps = 283 cps = 17,000 photopeak cpm.

In the absence of appreciable levels of interfering activities, it is found that a photopeak counting rate of as little as 10 cpm can be detected for an activity with a half-life longer than one hour. Thus, the estimated limit of detection (i.e., smallest amount detectable under the specified irradiation and counting conditions) for copper should be approximately:

10/17,000 μg, or about 0.00058 μg Cu.

This means that a Cu concentration as low as 0.00058 ppm (ppm = parts-per-million, where 1 ppm = 0.0001%) could be detected in a 1-gram sample, or as low as 0.58 ppm in a 1-milligram sample, or as low as 0.058% in a 1-microgram sample.

TABLE V

Calculated NAA Limits of Instrumental Detection for 70 Elements

Conditions:

Conditions: $\emptyset = 10^{13}$ n/cm²-sec (thermal neutrons)
$t_i = 1$ hour
Detection via NaI(Tl) (3″ x 3″)
gamma-ray spectrometry

Calcd. Limit of Detection, μg	Elements
1 — 3 x 10^{-6}	Dy
4 — 6 x 10^{-6}	
7 — 9 x 10^{-6}	Mn
1 — 3 x 10^{-5}	Co, Kr, Rh, In, Eu, Lu
4 — 6 x 10^{-5}	Sm, Ho, Hf, Ir, Au
7 — 9 x 10^{-5}	V, Ag, Cs
1 — 3 x 10^{-4}	Sc, Y, Ba, W, Re, Os
4 — 6 x 10^{-4}	Na, Cu, Ga, As, Sr, I
7 — 9 x 10^{-4}	Al, Br, La, Er
1 — 3 x 10^{-3}	Ge, Nb, Ru, Sb, Xe, Nd, Yb, Pt, Hg
4 — 6 x 10^{-3}	Ar, Pd, Te, Pr
7 — 9 x 10^{-3}	Mo, Gd
1 — 3 x 10^{-2}	F, Mg, Cl, Ti, Zn, Se, Cd, Sn, Ce, Tm, Ta, Pb
4 — 6 x 10^{-2}	K, Ni
7 — 9 x 10^{-2}	Rb
1 — 3 x 10^{-1}	Ca, Cr, Zr, Tb
4 — 6 x 10^{-1}	Ne
7 — 9 x 10^{-1}	
1 — 3	
4 — 6	
7 — 9	
1 — 3 x 10^1	Si, S, Fe

Median $\sim$ 0.002μg

The instrumental (gamma-ray spectrometry) limits of detection for 70 elements under these irradiation and counting conditions are summarized in Table V. A few ultrasensitive elements are seen to be detectable down to levels as low as about 10^{-6} μg, whereas a few rather insensitive elements can only be detected down to a level of about 10 μg. A typical, or median, limit of detection is about 0.002 μg. These calculated limits of detection are based upon the criteria cited by Buchanan (1961), which are: a minimum-detectable photopeak counting rate of 10 cpm for radionuclides with half lives longer than one hour, of 100 cpm for those with half lives between one minute and one hour, and of 1000 cpm for those with half lives between one second and one minute. Although these are the calculated limits of detection, most have been experimentally verified, at least approximately—see, for example, the work of Yule (1965).

Figure 4 is an illustrative view of a modern, pool-type, research nuclear reactor, the 250 kilowatt TRIGA Mark I reactor at the author's laboratory. In the pneumatic-tube irradiation position (used for work with induced activities with half lives in the range of seconds to minutes), the thermal-neutron flux is 2.5×10^{12} n/cm²-sec. In the 40-tube rotary specimen rack (used for work with longer-lived induced activities), the thermal-neutron flux is 1.8×10^{12} n/cm²-sec. With the pneumatic tube, samples and standards are briefly activated and counted one at a time. In the rotary specimen rack, anywhere from 1 to 40 samples (and standards) can be activated simultaneously at exactly the same thermal-neutron flux. Figure 4 shows the reactor core (which is 18 inches in diameter and contains about 75 ^{235}U-enriched fuel elements), as viewed from the top of the reactor pool through 16 feet of water, which is used as moderator, coolant, and shielding.

Figure 4. The TRIGA Mark I nuclear reactor.

At levels that are appreciably above the limits of detection, the precisions and accuracies attainable are ± a few percent of the value. If the interferences from one or more other induced activities are severe, even at optimum irradiation and decay times for the detection of a particularly induced activity of interest, such interferences can be removed by radiochemically separating the element of interest (with a carrier) from the interfering activities.

Where one wishes to detect and measure as many elements as possible in a sample —rather than just one or a few selected elements—a "scanning" procedure is used. This typically involves:

1. Activating the sample for a short time (seconds or minutes), and then quickly counting it on the gamma-ray spectrometer at one or two short decay times
2. Activating it next for 30 minutes or an hour, and then counting it at two or three longer decay times
3. Activating it finally for many hours (10-100), and then counting it at a few very long decay times (days to weeks).

This procedure optimizes the possible detection of:
1. Very short-lived induced activities (half-lives of seconds to minutes)
2. Medium-lived induced activities (half-lives of the order of hours)
3. Long-lived induced activities (half-lives of the order of days to months).

By using a NaI(Tl) detector and a 400-channel pulse-height analyzer, as many as 15 to 20 elements can sometimes be detected and measured in a single small sample —nondestructively. With a high-resolution lithium-drifted germanium detector (Ge(Li)) and a 4096-channel pulse-height analyzer, as many as 20-30 elements can sometimes be nondestructively detected and measured in a single small sample. (Rather long counting periods may be required, however, due to the relatively small size of even the largest Ge(Li) detectors currently available.) In scanning NAA measurements, the resulting pulse-height digital data are usually processed on a computer. The computer searches the data for all statistically significant peaks, measures their gamma-ray energies, determines the radionuclide responsible for each peak, and calculates (from a library of standard spectra and yields) the amount and concentration of each element detected, along with the standard deviation for each quantity. It can also compute a firm upper limit for the possible concentration of each of many undetected elements.

Forensic Neutron Activation Analysis

To date, the NAA technique has been applied to the analysis of many kinds of materials that are of importance as physical evidence in criminal and civil cases. The materials so studied to date include hair, blood, soil, marijuana, opium, bullet lead, gunshot residues, adhesive tape, paint, glass, paper, grease, oil, plastics, rubber, metals, and many others. Most of these have been studied, either briefly or extensively, in forensic NAA research investigations; however, many have also been investigated in connection with actual casework. At the present time, NAA results have been presented in United States courts in over 60 cases (Pro and Guinn, n.d.). The first one occurred in March 1964. There also have been a number of Canadian and British court cases, as well as a few in other countries. The status of this field of work, up to the fall of 1966, is presented in depth in the Proceedings of the First International Conference on Forensic Activation Analysis, a conference held at the author's laboratory in September 1966 (Guinn, editor, 1967).

All of the forensic applications are based upon the ultrasensitivity of high-flux NAA for a large number of elements, since this high sensitivity enables one to:

1. Analyze evidence specimens that are too small to be analyzed successfully by conventional analytical techniques
2. Detect and measure amounts of certain elements of interest (e.g., Ba and Sb in gunshot residues) that are present in amounts below the limit of detection by other methods
3. Detect and measure the concentrations of more elements than can be achieved by means of conventional analytical methods, especially characterizing trace elements in evidence samples that are being compared for possible "common origin."

Most, though not all, NAA forensic work uses the purely instrumental, nondestructive form of the method, that is based upon multichannel gamma-ray spectrometry of activated samples. This type of analysis, since it is nondestructive, has the additional advantage of preserving evidence specimens for possible later introduction in court, or for other analyses or examinations.

To date, the applications to tiny evidence specimens, or to tiny amounts of certain elements, have largely been in the area of gunshot studies. In the author's laboratory, an NAA technique has been developed to ascertain—with a high degree of probability—whether a person has recently fired a gun. It involves:

1. Removal of possible invisible gunshot residues from a portion of the back of the hand of a suspect (or victim in a questionable suicide case) with a "paraffin-lift" technique
2. Activation of the paraffin lift in the reactor for 30 minutes
3. Dissolution in acid of any possible gunshot-residue material present in the activated sample, along with carrier amounts of Ba^{+2} and Sb^{+3}
4. Separation of the Ba and Sb from one another, and from other activated elements (especially from 14.96-hour ^{24}Na and 37.29-minute ^{38}Cl, formed from the NaCl in perspiration from the skin)
5. Gamma-ray spectrometry measurement of any 82.9-minute ^{139}Ba ($E_\gamma = 0.166$ Mev) and 2.80-day ^{122}Sb ($E_\gamma = 0.564$ Mev) present.

Barium and antimony compounds are used in the primers of most United States, and of many foreign, cartridges, and small ($\sim\mu g$) amounts of these elements are deposited on the back of the gunhand in even a single firing of a typical revolver or automatic pistol. The amounts of Ba and Sb deposited, although quite small, are readily detected and measured by means of this high-flux NAA procedure. The amounts depend upon a number of variables such as the type and condition of the gun, the particular chamber fired, the brand of ammunition, and the wind direction and velocity. The work on gunshot residues has been reported in a number of papers by members of the author's group (Guinn, 1964a, 1964b, 1965, 1966, 1967b; Ruch et al., 1964; Ruch, Guinn, and Pinker, 1964; Bryan et al., 1965); the technique has been applied to actual criminal casework by the author's group, the United States Treasury Department, and others. Its use during an illustrative, actual case has been shown, as one of several examples, in a film on forensic activation analysis (anonymous, n.d.) prepared for the United States Atomic Energy Commission by the author's group. Several hundred paraffin-lift hand-sampling kits have been distributed by the author's laboratory to various United States and foreign law enforcement laboratories, and they are now frequently employed to sample the hands of suspects and victims in shooting cases—for possible NAA examination for Ba and Sb. Figures 5 and 6 show, respectively, the procedure for applying molten paraffin to the hand, and for removing the solidified paraffin from the hand of a suspect.

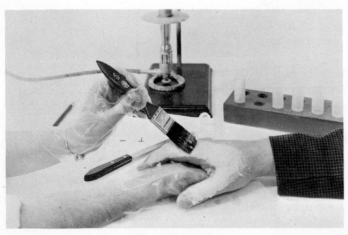

Figure 5. Application of paraffin to the hand of a suspect in a shooting case.

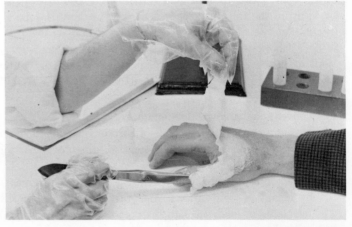

Figure 6. Removal of a paraffin lift from the hand of a suspect in a shooting case.

The gunshot-residue technique has also been applied, in a different form, to establish firing distances, and also to examine holes in various materials to establish whether they are bullet holes. The firing-distance technique is based upon the NAA work of Baumgaernter et al. (1963) in Germany, and which was developed further by Krishnan (1967a, 1967b) in Canada. It apparently is capable of determining the firing distance up to a distance of 8 or 10 feet. The application to the examination of possible bullet holes was developed in the United States by Schlesinger et al. (1967), by Krishnan (1967b), and by Krishnan and Nichol (1968) in Canada.

A somewhat related application is that of examining bullets and bullet fragments by NAA, which was developed by Lukens and Guinn (1967), and particularly by Lukens (1968). The principal element detected in such measurements is antimony, since manufacturers of bullet lead typically add from 0.5% to over 3% Sb to their lead in order to increase the bullet's hardness. Accurate measurement of the antimony content alone will usually determine whether two specimens are or are not of the same brand of ammunition—or whether they may be of the same brand. The measurement of two other elements that are sometimes added by manufacturers in sizeable amounts—arsenic and tin—and of a few trace elements often, or sometimes, detectable in bullet lead (i.e., Cu, Al, Ag) in addition to the Sb, will often make possible a more definitive "common origin" determination (meaning, in this case, bullets of a certain type made by the same manufacturer).

To date, most of the forensic activation analysis applications involve the principle of trace-element characterization. In effect, this principle states that, if two evidence specimens of a certain type of material (e.g., hair, marijuana, bullet lead, paint, glass, etc.) have a suitably defined "common origin," they will very closely show the same elemental composition not only in their major-element components ($> 1\%$), but also in their minor-element components ($0.01\text{-}1\%$), in their trace-element constituents (1-100 ppm), and in their ultra-trace-element constituents (< 1 ppm). If two specimens of different origin are of the same general kind of material, they may well have similar major-element compositions, but they will often show appreciable dissimilarities in elemental composition at the minor-element level and, essentially, always at the trace and ultra-trace levels.

No doubt the most fully-developed application of the NAA trace-element characterization approach at present is that involving the comparison of specimens of human head hair. This application was first developed by Jervis and co-workers, in Canada (Jervis et al., 1961; Perkons and Jervis, 1962, 1965; Jervis and Perkons, 1966; Perkons, 1965, 1967; Jervis, 1967). Other pertinent work on the NAA examination of hair specimens that may be cited here is reported in papers by Coleman (1966) and Coleman et al. (1967) in England and, in the United States, by Bate and Dyer (1965, 1967), by Bate (1965), and by Guinn (1967a). Altogether, some 29 elements have been detected in human head hair (Guinn, 1967a) by means of instrumental NAA. In any one specimen, fewer elements are detected—sometimes as many as 10-15 or more, the number depending upon the individual from whom the specimen came, the amount of sample, the cleaning method used, the severity of the irradiation, the nature and extent of the gamma-ray spectrometry employed, and the degree to which the resulting data are processed. Conditions for the proper NAA comparison of hair specimens involved in actual cases have been outlined in some detail by Guinn (1967a).

The NAA trace-element characterization studies have been reported on various other naturally occurring, evidence-type materials besides hair; e.g., on marijuana (Bryan et al., 1964-65), opium (Bate and Pro, 1964), and soil. For forensic purposes, soil is a difficult material because of its considerable heterogeneity and its variation in composition over very small lateral and vertical distances. A large amount of NAA data on blood may be found in the literature, but it is of little forensic use since:

1. Blood specimens associated with crime scenes are almost invariably contaminated with such things as dust, dirt, and cloth (and there is no way to "clean" such samples without also changing the composition of the blood specimen itself)
2. The Na^+ and Cl^- present in blood at appreciable and carefully body-regulated levels largely obscure upon neutron activation the instrumental detection of other trace elements that are possibly present, and which form short-lived or medium-lived (n, γ) products
3. Any nonessential, non-body-regulated, trace elements possibly present in the blood can vary widely from hour to hour, or day to day, in even the same individual, according to the nature of his food and drink.

The NAA approach to trace-element characterization has also been demonstrated to be fruitful with various kinds of manufactured materials of forensic interest—materials such as paint (Bryan et al., 1964-65; Bryan and Guinn, 1962-63, 1963-64, 1966; Guinn, 1966; Bryan, 1967), glass (Bryan and Guinn, 1966), paper (Bryan and Guinn, 1962-63; 1963-64; Bryan et al., 1964-65; Guinn, 1966), whisky, automobile greases (Bryan and Guinn, 1962-63), synthetic and processed rubber (Bryan and Guinn, 1962-63), inks (Bryan and Guinn, 1962-63), drugs (Bryan and Guinn, 1962-63), adhesive tape (Scott et al., 1967), etc. In general, it is found that even when two or more manufacturers endeavor to produce an essentially identical product, e.g., blue paint, or window glass, or amphetamines, etc., their respective products will show marked differences in their trace-element and ultra-trace-element compositions, and even though they may be very similar in their major-element and minor-element compositions. These differences are due to the different impurities in their respective raw materials, in their water and air, and in the elements that are contributed by the erosion and corrosion of their processing equipment.

Potential NAA Applications in the Field of Personal Identification in Mass Disasters

The possibility of applying forensic activation analysis techniques as an aid in the identification of mass disaster victims (burned or mutilated bodies, or fragments of bodies) has not as yet been explored. At first sight, a preliminary consideration of the identification problems that may exist in such mass disasters does not reveal any areas in which NAA techniques could be of help. A somewhat more detailed consideration, however, does reveal some possibilities, some of which are briefly mentioned below. It seems likely that, if a real effort were made to explore these possibilities—and others that would no doubt evolve from such efforts—some useful applications of the NAA techniques to mass-disaster personal identification problems would result.

If hair specimens suitable for analysis are available, one possible application is identification by means of hair comparisons. Just as fingerprints, per se, are of no identification value unless they can be compared with known fingerprints of the same individual (such as in the FBI fingerprint files), a measured hair composition is of no identification value unless it can be compared with the hair known to have come from a specified individual. In some instances, a hair comparison sample can be obtained from a recently used comb or brush in the home of the deceased person. If at least some of the hair on the head of the body is not burned or badly contaminated, it can be cleaned, examined under the microscope, and then compared via NAA with the appropriate hair specimens, similarly treated, that have been obtained from the comb or brush known to have been recently used by the person thought to be the victim. Some of the factors involved in making valid hair comparisons in such cases (e.g., not comparing living hairs with dead hairs) have been discussed by the author (Guinn, 1967a). The number of trace elements detectable in human head hair is quite large (Perkons, 1967; Guinn, 1967a), the concentration of any particular element in the hair varies widely from one person to another (and much less widely amongst the individual head hairs of one particular person), and the various element concentrations found exhibit, in most instances, only small element-element correlations. Thus, with appropriate samples to work with, and with proper techniques, one has a considerable number of points of comparison (accurately and precisely measured element concentrations) that can be made between any two hair specimens. Amongst other things, the number of elements that are detectable in a specimen of hair will increase with increasing sample size. With considerable effort (long irradiation at a high thermal-neutron flux and long counting periods) anywhere from 6 to 8 elements can typically be detected in even a 1 cm strand of hair. With larger samples, upward of 15 elements can sometimes be detected in a single sample.

Thus, under the proper conditions, if two hair specimens are found to agree quite closely in their respective concentrations (of many elements with no significant disparities), one can estimate, to a high degree of probability, that the two specimens came from the same person. Conversely, and under the proper conditions, if two hair specimens exhibit widely different compositions, one can conclude that they came from different persons.

At present, there is only a limited amount of NAA experimental information on the trace-element concentrations—and their person-to-person variability—of pubic hairs and other human body hairs, of human fingernails and toenails, and of animal hairs from different animal species.

A second possibility for the useful application of NAA techniques is that of analyzing objects and materials found on bodies to establish their elemental composition. Such objects and materials might include such things as rings, eyeglasses, eyeglass frames, buttons, shoe leather, belt leather, belt buckles, various items of clothing, etc. It is assumed here, of course, that such items would already have been visually examined by investigators, and by members of the families of the various deceased individuals, without any resulting positive identification. It is also assumed that other types of relevant forensic examination and analysis would also be employed; i.e., not only NAA. If even a combination of the other approaches fails to result in a positive identification, however, a neutron activation analysis examination might be warranted and might be fruitful. The materials analyzed could be compared with corresponding materials of the same brands known to have been worn by the deceased. If quite a number of diverse items found on a body could be shown to be of the same respective commercial brands as were known to be worn by the deceased, a reasonably firm identification of the body could be made. In regular forensic activation analysis studies of actual cases, analogous applications have been made in the author's laboratory to buttons and cloth.

A third possibility is a very specialized one, one that came close to being used in a commercial aircraft mass disaster several years ago. This California crash was caused by the pilot and co-pilot being shot by one of the passengers. Just before the crash, the pilot radioed that he had been shot and that the plane was going to crash. Everyone on board was killed in the crash. The bodies of the pilot and co-pilot, with bullet holes in them, were found in the wreckage. One gun was also found amongst the wreckage. Many of the bodies were fragmented. Part of one hand was found, and, via fingerprint comparison in the FBI files, it was found to belong to one passenger who was suspected of having done the shooting. The investigating agency asked the author if a gunshot-residue examination, via NAA, of the back of this hand could ascertain whether or not this hand had recently fired a gun. This would have been possible, except for the fact that the hand was so encrusted with blood and mud that analysis was not feasible. Such an approach, however, could be of use in some future case if the resulting hand specimens to be examined for gunshot residues are not contaminated with extraneous materials. If the recent and present rash of airliner hijackings to Havana is not curbed soon, there is a distinct possibility that some hijacker may panic and shoot the flight crew, which would result in a crash similar to the California crash.

Literature Cited

Anonymous
  n.d.   The Nuclear Witness; Activation Analysis in Crime Investigation. U.S. Atomic Energy film produced by General Atomic (28-minute, 16-mm., color-sound film; copies can be borrowed from the U.S. AEC).

Bate, L. C.
  1965.   The Use of Activation Analysis in Procedures for the Removal and Characterization of the Surface Contaminants of Hair. *Journal of Forensic Sciences*, 10:60-72.

Bate, L. C., and Dyer, F. F.
  1965.   Trace Elements in Human Hair. *Nucleonics*, 23 (10): 74-81.
  1967.   *Forensic Applications of Trace Elements in Hair.* Report GA-8171, Gulf General Atomic, San Diego, Calif., pp. 247-259.

Bate, L. C., and Pro, M. J.
  1964.   Application of Activation Analysis to Forensic Science. II. Drugs. *International Journal of Applied Radiation and Isotopes*, 15:111-114.

Baumgaertner, F.; Stark, H.; and Schoentag, A.
  1963.   Activation Analysis Determination of Antimony in the Nanogram Range for Determination of Firing Distance. *Zeitschrift für Analytische Chemie*, 197:424-30.

Bryan, D. E.
  1967.   *The Comparison of Paint Samples by Neutron Activation Analysis.* Report GA-8171, Gulf General Atomic, San Diego, Calif., pages 133-44.

Byran, D. E., and Guinn, V. P.
  1962-1963.   *Applications of Neutron Activation Analysis in Scientific Crime Detection.* Report GA-5556, Gulf General Atomic, San Diego, Calif.
  1963-1964.   *Use of Neutron Activation Analysis in Scientific Crime Detection.* Report GA-6152, Gulf General Atomic, San Diego, Calif.
  1966.   Forensic Activation Analysis: Trace-Level Elements in Commercial Paints. *Transactions of the American Nuclear Society*, 9:589.

Bryan, D. E.; Guinn, V. P.; and Settle, D. M.
  1964-1965.   *Applications of Neutron Activation Analysis in Scientific Crime Detection.* Report GA-7041, Gulf General Atomic, San Diego, Calif.
  1965.   New Developments in the Application of Neutron Activation Analysis to Problems in Scientific Crime Detection. *Proceedings of the International Conference on Modern Trends in Activation Analysis* (Texas Agricultural and Mechanical College of Texas), pp. 140-5.

Buchanan, J. D.
  1961.   Activation Analysis with a TRIGA Reactor. *Proceedings of the International Conference on Modern Trends in Activation Analysis* (Texas Agricultural and Mechanical College of Texas), pages 72-7. (Also as General Atomic Report GA-2662).

Coleman, R. F.
  1966.   The Application of Neutron Activation Analysis to Forensic Science. *Journal of the Forensic Science Society*, 6:19-27.

Coleman, R. F.; Cripps, H. F.; Stinson, A.; and Scott, H. D.
  1967.   *The Trace-Element Content of Human Head Hair in England and Wales, and the Application to Forensic Science.* Report GA-8171, Gulf General Atomic, San Diego, Calif., pages 203-19.

Goldman, D. T., and Stehn, J. R.
  n.d.   *Chart of the Nuclides.* General Electric Co., San Jose, Calif.

Guinn, V. P.
  1964a.   Recent Developments in the Application of Neutron Activation Analysis Techniques to Forensic Problems. *Journal of the Forensic Science Society*, 4:184-91.
  1964b.   Non-Biological Applications of Neutron Activation Analysis in Forensic Studies. Chapter in *Methods of Forensic Science*, III. Edited by A. S. Curry. Interscience Publishers, London, pages 47-68.
  1965.   Forensic Applications of Activation Analysis. Chapter in *Activation Analysis; Principles and Applications*. Edited by J. M. A. Lenihan and S. J. Thomson. Academic Press, London, pages 125-7.
  1966a.   New Developments in the Application of Activation Analysis to Problems in Crime Investigation. *Proceedings of the Seventh Japan Conference on Radioisotopes* (Tokyo), pages 563-9.
  1966b.   *Applications of Neutron Activation Analysis in Scientific Crime Detection.* Report GA-8013, Gulf General Atomic, San Diego, Calif.
  1967a.   *Neutron Activation Analysis and its Forensic Applications.* Report GA-8171, Gulf General Atomic, San Diego, Calif., pages 7-39.

1967b. *The Determination of Traces of Barium and Antimony in Gunshot Residues by Activation Analysis.* Report GA-8171, Gulf General Atomic, San Diego, Calif., pages 161-76.

Guinn, V. P. (editor)
1967. *Proceedings of the First International Conference on Forensic Activation Analysis.* Report GA-8171, Gulf General Atomic, San Diego, Calif.

Heath, R. L.
1964. *Scintillation Spectrometry Gamma-Ray Spectrum Catalogue.* 2d edition. Volumes 1 and 2 (IDO-16880-1 and -2). Office of Technical Services, U.S. Department of Commerce, Washington, D.C.

Jervis, R. E.
1967. *The Value of Neutron Activation Analysis Hair Comparisons in Forensic Investigations; a Critique.* Report GA-8171, Gulf General Atomic, San Diego, Calif., pages 287-94.

Jervis, R. E., and Perkons, A. K.
1966. Trace Elements in Human Head Hair. *Journal of Forensic Sciences,* 11:50-63.

Jervis, R. E.; Perkons, A. K.; Mackintosh, W. D.; and Kerr, F. M.
1961. Activation Analysis in Forensic Investigation. *Proceedings of the International Conference on Modern Trends in Activation Analysis* (Texas Agricultural and Mechanical University), pages 107-13.

Krishnan, S. S.
1967a. *Distance Determination of Gunshot Firings by Neutron Activation Analysis.* Report GA-8171, Gulf General Atomic, San Diego, Calif., pp. 177-87.
1967b. Determination of Gunshot Firing Distances and Identification of Bullet Holes by Neutron Activation Analysis. *Journal of Forensic Sciences,* 12:112-22.

Krishnan, S. S., and Nichol, R. C.
1968. Identification of Bullet Holes by Neutron Activation Analysis and Autoradiography. *Journal of Forensic Sciences,* 13:519-27.

Lederer, C. M.; Hollander, J. M.; and Perlman, I.
1967. *Table of Isotopes.* 6th edition. John Wiley & Sons, N.Y.

Lukens, H. R.
1968. Forensic Activation Analysis: Bullet Lead. *Transactions of the American Nuclear Society,* 11:80-1.

Lukens, H. R., and Guinn, V. P.
1967. Neutron Activation Analysis of Bullet Lead. *Transactions of the American Nuclear Society,* 10:66-7.

Perkons, A. K.
1965. *Hair Individualization Study by Neutron Activation.* Ph.D. thesis, University of Toronto.
1967. *Individualization of Human Head Hair.* Report GA-8171, Gulf General Atomic, San Diego, Calif., pp. 221-35.

Perkons, A. K., and Jervis, R. E.
1962. Applications of Radio-Activation Analysis in Forensic Investigations. *Journal of Forensic Sciences,* 7:449-464.
1965. Hair Individualization Studies. *Proceedings of the International Conference on Modern Trends in Activation Analysis* (Texas Agricultural and Mechanical College of Texas), pages 295-303.

Pro, M. J., and Guinn, V. P.
n.d. *A List of U.S. Court Cases in Which Activation Analysis Results Were Successfully Introduced.* (Updated version available from either author.)

Ruch, R. R.; Buchanan, J. D.; Pinker, R. H.; Guinn, V. P.; and Bellanca, S. C.
1964. Neutron Activation Analysis in Scientific Crime Detection; Some Recent Developments. *Journal of Forensic Sciences,* 9:119-33.

Ruch, R. R.; Guinn, V. P.; and Pinker, R. H.
1964. Detection of Gunpowder Residues by Neutron Activation Analysis. *Nuclear Science and Engineering,* 20:381-5.

Schlesinger, H. L.; Hoffman, C. M.; and Pro, M. J.
1967. *Bullet Residue Transference to Various Materials.* Report GA-8171, Gulf General Atomic, San Diego, Calif., pp. 189-97.

Scott, J. E.; Hoffman, C. M.; Pro, M. J.; and Schlesinger, H. L.
1967. Comparison of Adhesive Tapes by Neutron Activation Analysis. *Journal of the Association of Official Analytical Chemists,* 50:371-6.

Yule, H. P.
1965. Experimental Reactor Thermal-Neutron Activation Analysis Sensitivities. *Analytical Chemistry,* 37:129-32.

Use of Drug Detection in Mass Casualty Identification *

Leo R. Goldbaum

Since 1956 the Armed Forces Institute of Pathology has provided pathologic and toxicologic support in the medical investigation of aircraft accidents (Stembridge, Crafft, and Townsend, 1958). Although many of these accidents resulted in mass casualties, the remains of the crew members were the primary subjects of toxicologic examination. This is due to the need to determine the role of human failure in the cause of the accidents. It soon became apparent, however, that the toxicologic evaluation of specimens obtained from all such victims required a different approach from that used in most forensic work. The drug levels involved are the low ones that result from therapeutic ingestion, rather than the much higher ones that result from overdoses associated with accidental or deliberate poisonings. Accordingly, a procedure had to be developed to detect drugs when they were present in biologic samples in the low concentrations that result from therapeutic dosages; i.e., concentrations that range from a high of 1 ug/ml, or gm, for a large number of drugs, to as low as 0.1 ug/ml, or gm, for many other drugs.

This experience in aircraft accident toxicology investigations was so successful at the AFIP that wider application is now possible. Like blood groups, tissue drug levels provide a means to differentiate between victims who are grossly indistinguishable. But also like blood groups, which are useful for identification only when records exist, tissue drug levels depend for their interpretation upon the knowledge that certain individuals were using particular drugs.

In this paper, very little space will be devoted to analytic procedures, since these must be carried out in well-equipped laboratories by trained personnel who will have access to the technical literature (Goldbaum and Domanski, 1965a and b, 1966). The main purpose here is to report some laboratory findings on crash victims who had taken drugs in therapeutic dosages, and to illustrate thereby how this method of identification works. The method would seem to have considerable application in the identification of disaster victims who are military personnel, since these individuals are so often engaged in foreign areas where drugs are frequently used to protect against, or cure, diseases.

Sample Collection

It is important that the tissues submitted for analysis have not undergone decomposition, and that they have been contaminated as little as possible by the accident, during the autopsy, or in the process of collection, storage, and shipment to the laboratory. The amount of any one tissue sent for analysis should be at least 50 gm; all the available blood and urine should also be sent. The specimens should be frozen in dry ice in plastic containers.

*Supported in part by the Air Force grant AF MIPR AM 5-40048, from the USAF Aerospace Medical Research Laboratory, Brooks Air Force Base, Texas.

Outline of Analytic Procedure

The commonly used therapeutic agents are separated into three groups:

1. Acid drugs (barbiturates, salicylates)
2. Basic drugs (tranquilizers, antihistamines, antimalarials, analgesics)
3. Neutral drugs (meprobamates, Doriden).

After extracts have been obtained from the homogenated tissue samples with ether, they are subjected to various purification techniques, and then the presence, or absence, of the reported drugs is determined primarily by ultraviolet spectroscopy, gas chromatography, and chemical tests. In some instances, spectrofluometric analysis and infrared absorption spectroscopy are used. The analytical procedure requires approximately two days.

Examples of Identification by Drug Detection

Illustrated below are representative aircraft accident cases in which drugs have been observed in the tissue samples of fatalities. The cases have been selected to represent the classes of most commonly prescribed pharmacologic agents; e.g., anorexiants, antimalarials, tranquilizers, antihistaminics, and antidepressants. The drug concentrations given are, of course, those for the individuals who were taking the medications.

Aircraft Accident Case No. 1
(Two occupants, one treated for a cold with a decongestant and bronchodilator.)

Drug reported used: *Sudafed.*
  Concentrations found:

Liver	1.0	mg/100gm	Lung	0.8	mg/100gm
Brain	0.2	mg/100gm	Blood	0.12	mg/100gm
Fat	0.02	mg/100gm	Urine	30.0	mg/100gm
Kidney	2.2	mg/100gm	Stom. Cont.	0.1	mg/100gm

Drug reported used: *Chlor-Trimeton.*
  Concentrations found:

Liver	0.2	mg/100gm
Brain	0.1	mg/100gm

Aircraft Accident Case No. 2
(Three occupants, one taking an antihistamine.)

Drug reported used: *Chlor-Trimeton.*
  Concentrations found:

Lung	0.15	mg/100gm	Kidney	0.25	mg/100gm
Brain	0.14	mg/100gm	Blood	0.02	mg/100gm
Liver	0.30	mg/100gm			

Aircraft Accident Case No. 3
(Two occupants, one taking antidepressants.)

Drug reported used: *Amphetamine.*
  Concentrations found:

Liver	0.05	mg/100gm
Lung	0.03	mg/100gm
Kidney	0.03	mg/100gm

Drug reported used: *Elavil.*
  Concentrations found:

Liver	0.1	mg/100gm
Lung	0.05	mg/100gm
Kidney	0.05	mg/100gm

Aircraft Accident Case No. 4
(Three occupants, one taking an antimalarial.)

Drug reported used: *Chloroquine.*
Concentrations found:

Urine	3.5 mg/100gm	Brain	4.5 mg/100gm
Liver	13.6 mg/100gm	Lung	7.5 mg/100gm
Kidney	4.6 mg/100gm		

Aircraft Accident Case No. 5
(Three occupants, one taking medication for a mild depressive state.)

Drug reported used: *Amobarbital.*
Concentrations found:

Heart	0.40 mg/100gm	Lung	0.30 mg/100gm
Kidney	0.20 mg/100gm	Fat (heart)	1.0 mg/100gm
Liver	0.50 mg/100gm		

Drug reported used: *Amphetamine.*
Concentrations found:

Kidney	0.1 mg/100gm
Lung	0.06 mg/100gm
Liver	0.1 mg/100gm

Aircraft Accident Case No. 6
(Three occupants, one taking a tranquilizer.)

Drug reported used: *Meprobamate.*
Concentrations found:

Lung	0.4 mg/100gm
Spleen	0.6 mg/100gm
Liver	0.6 mg/100gm

Aircraft Accident Case No. 7
(Three occupants, one taking an anorexiant for appetite control.)

Drug reported used: *Phentermine Resin (Ionamin).*
Concentrations found:

Liver	0.40 mg/100gm	Stom. Cont.	03.0 mg/100gm
Kidney	0.25 mg/100gm	Blood	sample too small
Brain	0.08 mg/100gm		for quantitation

Detection of Other Drugs in Tissues

Besides the commonly prescribed pharmacologic agents, the products of tobacco smoke can be found in certain tissues; for example, nicotine in the urine and carbon monoxide in the blood. This offers a means to differentiate the remains of smokers and nonsmokers. The concentration of carbonoxyhemoglobin in smokers ranges from 2% to 10% of the total hemoglobin. In nonsmokers, it is less than 1%. Nicotine is present in the urine only of smokers.

Conclusion

Recently developed toxicologic procedures make it possible to determine in tissues the low level presence of many common drugs. Hence, information about drug use by any of the victims in a mass disaster increases the possibility of their identification.

Literature Cited

Goldbaum, L. R., and Domanski, T. J.
  1965a Aerospace Toxicology Procedures: Current Practices and Trends at the Armed Forces Institute of Pathology. *Aerospace Medicine,* 36 (7): 662-4.
  1965b An Approach to the Analysis of Biological Specimens for Basic Drugs. *In Progress in Chemical Toxicology,* ed. by A. Stolman, II: 221-38.
  1966 Detection and Identification of Micrograms of Neutral Drugs in Biological Samples. *Journal of Forensic Sciences,* 11 (2):233-42.
Stembridge, V. A.; Crafft, W. M.; and Townsend, F. M.
  1958 Medical Investigation of Aircraft Accidents with Multiple Casualties. *Journal of Aviation Medicine,* 29:668-675.

Estimation of Skeletal Age:
From Puberty to About 30 Years of Age

Thomas W. McKern

For the physical anthropologist, man ages in not one, but two different ways. First, he matures chronologically; i.e., as he calculates his age from his date of birth. Chronological age differs not at all between the sexes. Second, he matures physiologically, age being judged—by x-ray during life, or by gross inspection of bone after death—subjectively, with reference to sex, from the stages of growth and development in the skeleton.

For normal individuals, the two aging scales are generally in accord; however, in dealing with unknown remains—a task looming large in the workload of forensic pathologists and physical anthropologists—there is no way to tell which individuals are normal and which are abnormal so far as osseous development is concerned. Hence, there is no way to determine whether estimated physiological ages accurately correspond to actual chronological age.

Much of our early information about skeletal maturation was derived from a doubtfully documented cadaver series, where true age was an approximation at best and, in many cases, was totally unsubstantiated. This led to errors in the chronological age assessments for unknown remains in every decade of life. The best that can be done to offset such errors is to improve the estimates of physiological or skeletal age. Accordingly, the purpose of the present paper is to give some of the principal guidelines for skeletal aging that have been established. Males alone will be considered. There are as yet no equivalent data for females.

The first opportunity afforded identification experts to test current aging techniques was provided by the Memorial Division, Office of the Quartermaster General. Following World War II, the Memorial Division established identification laboratories at various sites in Europe and in the Pacific, where American war dead were identified and processed for shipment back to the United States.

Even greater opportunities came in 1953, when Operation Glory was initiated following the Korean conflict. Dr. T. Dale Stewart of the Smithsonian Institution was selected to direct research on identification problems in connection with the recovery of the American war dead in Korea. At the Central Identification Laboratory located in Kokura, Japan, Dr. Stewart was able to record a vast amount of information, to collect photographs, and to prepare casts to represent most of the evidence of skeletal age changes in 450 individuals. These data were later forwarded to the Smithsonian Institution in Washington, D.C.

In 1955, the author joined Dr. Stewart in an intensive analysis of the results of his most thorough efforts. For the first time, detailed data were available on a large documented sample of male skeltons between the ages of 17 and 50 years. It was now possible to:

1. Check aging criteria
2. Test the reliability of techniques used for age estimation
3. Initiate research for new techniques.

Results of the analysis were most enlightening, and a detailed report was published (McKern and Stewart, 1957). The sections that now follow focus upon the conclusions reached in regard to each of the skeletal areas studied.

A few points should be noted. First, since the evidence for developmental processes may be present within bone, even when the unaided eye can distinguish no changes, skeletal age is ideally judged from the inspection of both the gross bones and the radiographs thereof. This has never been done on a large number of subjects, and it was not undertaken on the war dead due to the inadequacy of the x-ray facilities that were available at the identification laboratory in Japan. For this reason, gross bone inspection constitutes the sole basis for the present guidelines.

Second, the period of aging under present consideration—from puberty until about 30 years—very nearly represents that observed for the union of the various epiphyses. Indeed, most of the findings covered here concern epiphyseal union. Since the ages of the American war dead studied did not extend below 17 years, the lower limit of the period is ill defined: for purposes of convenience, it is referred to as "puberty," somewhere between 13 and 15 years. The upper limit of epiphyseal activity in males does not extend beyond 30 years; for the great majority of cases, the upper limit may well be as low as 28 years. Thus, the lower part of the epiphyseal union period overlaps the period when dental eruption and root ossification provide the best age indicators; and the upper part finds the bones ripe for the onset of degenerative changes.

Until the appearance of the McKern-Stewart report in 1957, the most widely used guidelines for skeletal aging were those originally published by Krogman in 1939, and these were based upon the work of T. Wingate Todd and his associates at the Western Reserve Medical School. For many of the major epiphyses, Krogman cited a two-year interval of union. This implied—in the minds of many researchers—that all normal individuals of the same sex undergo complete union of a particular epiphysis while passing through a certain two-year age interval. We now know that the intervals may last as long as 6 or 7 years; establishing this fact of high variability was a primary contribution of the Korean study (see Figure 7). Recently (1962), Krogman clarified his earlier report by stating that the short, two-year intervals were intended to represent only "central tendencies." This new recognition of the variability in the aging process now forces observers of epiphyseal union to be more generous in stating the probable error of their age estimates than in the past.

The following analysis of the collected data is divided into an arbitrary sequence of different parts of the skeleton. For age identification, particularly where remains may be fragmentary, an understanding of the maturational activity for separate body parts is essential. Emphasis, however, is placed upon the combined maturational activity, and upon new techniques that permit reliable age determinations to be made from certain critical, single factors.

Eruption of Third Molars

It is generally recognized that the eruption pattern of the third molars is extremely irregular. This situation is reflected in many textbooks where the eruption of the third molars is stated as a time interval rather than a mean age. Cunningham's *Textbook of Anatomy*, for example, cites the age of eruption as 17-21 years; *Gray's Anatomy* states the interval as 17-25 years. Obviously, such data are of limited use in cases of individual identification.

Besides erupting late and slowly, the third molars often do not erupt normally, especially in the lower jaw where, because of an evolutionary reduction in length, the third molars may be forced out of normal alignment. In other cases, both upper and lower third molars may fail to erupt or, relatively often, even fail to form (congenital absence). In such cases during life, gross inspection may not reveal the presence of some, or all, of the third molars, and hence they may be reported as absent when in fact they are only hidden.

YEARS

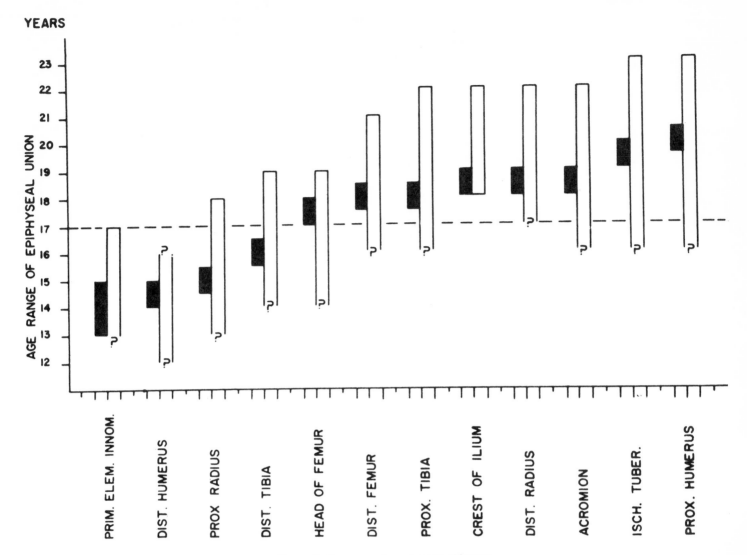

Figure 7. The expanding concept of human variability as it relates to epiphyseal union. Comparison of age ranges obtained by Krogman (1939) and by McKern and Stewart (1957). *Solid bars* = Krogman; *open bars* = McKern and Stewart (from Stewart, 1963, Fig. 2.).

Despite these irregularities, the eruption of these teeth is one of the last maturational events, and this makes them feasible supplementary age indicators. Table VI, which demonstrates the status of the third molars between the ages of 17 and 50, shows that this is indeed the case. The main eruption period is 17-22 years, but at the peak of eruption (17-18 years) only a little over half of the upper, and one-third of the lower, molars give a clue to age. Also, although eruption generally ceases at 22 years, a few cases may be found in unerupted and erupting stages as late as 35 years.

We must conclude, therefore, that as age indicators the third molars provide only a supplementary utility, one that is best used in connection with supporting data from other maturative events. Fortunately, the beginning of epiphyseal union overlaps the conclusion of tooth eruption.

TABLE VI
The Status of the Third Molars by Age Groups*
(in %)

| | | Unerupted | | | | Partially erupted | | | | Impacted | | | | Normally erupted | | | | Absent | | | |
| | | Upper | | Lower | | Upper | | Lower | | Upper | | Lower | | Upper | | Lower | | Upper | | Lower | |
Age	No.	R	L	R	L	R	L	R	L	R	L	R	L	R	L	R	L	R	L	R	L
17-18	55	18	20	18	18	40	35	18	14	—	—	18	22	20	19	28	21	22	26	18	25
19	52	6	2	4	—	29	31	16	18	—	—	12	16	40	42	38	37	25	25	30	29
20	45	5	7	5	6	24	20	5	8	—	—	14	15	54	50	54	47	17	23	22	24
21	39	3	—	—	6	8	13	13	11	6	3	11	11	39	58	46	34	44	26	30	38
22	25	—	—	—	—	8	16	8	8	—	—	4	—	52	52	56	48	40	32	32	44
23	27	4	—	—	—	—	—	—	4	—	—	—	4	59	70	67	66	37	30	33	26
24-25	28	4	4	4	4	7	7	7	10	10	—	14	—	27	40	32	43	52	49	43	43
26-27	25	4	—	—	—	4	8	—	—	—	—	4	4	32	36	44	44	60	56	52	52
28-30	29	4	—	—	4	4	7	4	11	—	—	4	—	55	55	56	44	37	38	36	41
31-40	43	2	2	—	2	2	7	2	—	5	—	5	5	45	44	40	45	46	47	53	48
41-50	6	—	—	—	—	—	—	—	—	—	—	—	—	33	17	33	17	67	83	67	83
Total	375																				

*After Table 17, page 40, McKern and Stewart, 1957.

Epiphyses

The three major bones that comprise each of the four extremities are called *long bones*. Each long bone is made up of a *diaphysis* (shaft) with one or more *epiphyses* at either end. Thus, the long bones grow in two dimensions: in girth and in length (by means of the epiphyses). Growth in length ceases when the epiphyses fuse with the diaphysis.

Since epiphyseal union proceeds at varying rates, it is usually recorded on a scale of 0-4.

0 = non-union
1 = one-fourth united
2 = one-half united
3 = three-quarters united
4 = complete union

Observations on union patterns for the long bones are summarized in Tables VII and VIII.

It will be noted that at 17 and 18 years of age, the epiphyses of the ankle, hip, and elbow are already in the late stages of union. These are completely fused by 20 years of age, whereas the epiphyses of the knee, wrist, and shoulder demonstrate early stages of union throughout the late teens and early twenties. Complete fusion occurs between 23 and 24 years of age. Again, the variability of these events is greater than that which was anticipated prior to the analysis.

TABLE VII*
The Age Distribution of Complete Union for
The Long Bone Epiphyses (in %)

| | | Upper Extremity | | | Lower Extremity | | | | |
| | | Humerus: med. epicond. | Radius: prox. | Ulna: prox. | Femur: | | | Tibia: dist. | Fibula: dist. |
Age	No.				head	gtr. troch.	lsr. troch.		
17-18	55	86	93	90	88	88	88	89	89
19	52	96	100	100	96	98	98	98	94
20	45	100			100	100	100	100	100
Total	152								

*After Table 20, page 44, McKern and Stewart, 1957.

TABLE VIII*
The Age Distribution for Stages of Union for
The Long Bone Epiphyses (in %)

		Upper Extremity															Lower Extremity														
		Humerus (prox.)					Radius (dist.)					Ulna (dist.)					Femur (dist.)					Tibia (prox.)					Fibula (prox.)				
		Stages					Stages					Stages					Stages					Stages					Stages				
Age	No.	0	1	2	3	4	0	1	2	3	4	0	1	2	3	4	0	1	2	3	4	0	1	2	3	4	0	1	2	3	4
17-18	55	14	5	25	35	21	22	3	14	32	29	29	1	11	24	35	16	2	3	18	61	2	2	7	23	66	14	—	3	12	71
19	52	5	2	10	58	25	7	—	5	48	40	7	—	5	32	56	4	—	1	9	86	1	—	1	17	81	4	—	6	4	86
20	45	2	2	4	40	52	4	—	2	24	70	4	2	—	24	70			2	9	89				13	87			2	—	98
21	37			2	27	71				19	81				10	90				8	92				5	95				5	95
22	24				12	88				12	88				8	92					100				4	96					100
23	26				4	96					100					100										100					
24 +	136					100																									
Total	375																														

*After Table 21, page 45, McKern and Stewart, 1957.

TABLE IX*
Epiphysis on Iliac Crest: Age Distribution
of Stages of Union (in %)

		Stages of Union				
Age	No.	0	1	2	3	4
17	10	40	10	10	40	—
18	45	18	16	26	20	20
19	52	5	4	27	28	36
20	45	2	6	4	24	64
21	37	—	5	8	13	74
22	24	—	—	4	4	92
23	26	—	—	—	—	100
	Total 239					

* After Table 22, page 61, McKern and Stewart, 1957.

Innominate

The distribution of the stages of union for the epiphyses on the iliac crest and the ischium are found in Tables IX and X. Despite a pattern of irregularity, the general picture for both epiphyses is one of fairly rapid progress, with a period of greatest activity between 20 and 21 years of age, and with complete union occurring by the age of 23 years.

TABLE X*
Epiphysis on Ischium: Age Distribution
of Stages of Union
(in %)

		Stages of Union				
Age	No.	0	1	2	3	4
17	10	50	10	20	10	10
18	45	52	13	12	12	11
19	52	14	24	13	17	32
20	45	11	13	9	23	44
21	37	10	6	3	25	56
22	24	4	—	—	4	92
23	26	—	—	4	4	92
24-25	27	—	—	—	—	100
	Total 266					

* After Table 24, page 69, McKern and Stewart, 1957.

Clavicle

Table XI summarizes the age distribution of the stages of union for the medial clavicular epiphysis, both right and left, from our series. As early as 18 years, but at any time between 18 and 25 years, the epiphyseal cap begins to unite to the medial end of the clavicle. Greatest activity occurs between 24 and 25 years; union is complete by 31 years of age.

TABLE XI*
Age Distribution of The Stages of Union for The Medial Clavicular Epiphysis (in %)

Age	No.	Right Stage of Union					Left Stage of Union				
		0	1	2	3	4	0	1	2	3	4
17	10	—	—	—	—	—	—	—	—	—	—
18	45	90	10	—	—	—	86	12	2	—	—
19	52	79	13	8	—	—	73	21	4	—	—
20	45	69	28	11	2	—	56	35	7	2	—
21	37	36	43	13	8	—	47	32	13	8	—
22	24	4	27	39	30	—	1	33	37	29	—
23	26	—	11	43	40	6	—	8	43	40	9
24-25	27	—	3	10	52	37	—	3	10	52	37
26-27	25	—	—	—	36	64	—	—	—	36	64
28-29	18	—	—	—	31	69	—	—	—	31	69
30	11	—	—	—	9	91	—	—	—	9	91
31	54	—	—	—	—	100	—	—	—	—	100
Total	374										

* After Table 28, page 91, McKern and Stewart, 1957.

Vertebral Column

The presacral vertebral column is completely ossified by 24 years of age. Table XII illustrates the age distribution of stages of union for the superior and inferior epiphyseal rings, whereas Table XIII demonstrates the same information for the epiphyses of the vertebral spines.

TABLE XII*
The Age Distribution of Stages of Union for The Superior and Inferior Epiphyseal Rings of The Pre-Sacral Column as a Whole (in %)

Age	No.	Superior Surface Stages					Inferior Surface Stages				
		0	1	2	3	4	0	1	2	3	4
17-18	54	5	22	37	23	13	2	24	37	23	13
19	50		10	30	36	24		8	32	48	14
20	43		7	14	33	46		7	14	37	42
21	35			20	27	63			20	36	44
22	24			4	8	88			4	8	88
23	26				7	93				11	89
24-25	27					100					100
Total	259										

* After Table 31, page 99, McKern and Stewart, 1957.

TABLE XIII*
Age Distribution of Stages of Union for The
Epiphyses of The Vertebral Spines (in %)

Age	No.	Stages 0	1	2	3	4
17-18	52	21	16	20	18	25
19	51	7	10	15	27	41
20	42	4	3	7	14	72
21	34			11	12	77
22	23				4	96
23	26				3	97
24-25	27					100
Total	255					

* After Table 33, page 102, McKern and Stewart, 1957.

Noteworthy is the sequential ossification pattern, which shows that the last signs of complete union occur in the upper thoracic vertebrae, particularly in T-4 and T-5.

Scapula

Since the epiphyses for both the coracoid process and the glenoid margin usually unite before the initial age in our series, stages of union were recorded for the acromion, inferior angle, and medial border only. Table XIV summarizes these observations.

TABLE XIV*
Age Distribution of Stages of Epiphyseal Union for The
Acromion, Inferior Angle, and Medial Border of The Scapula (in %)

Age	No.	Acromion 0	1	2	3	4	Inferior Angle 0	1	2	3	4	Medial Border 0	1	2	3	4
17	10	50	—	—	10	40	50	10	—	—	40	60	—	—	10	20
18	38	20	4	4	8	64	38	8	2	12	40	46	10	8	10	26
19	51	10	2	2	4	82	21	—	4	11	64	30	—	10	15	46
20	43	4	—	2	11	83	9	—	—	4	87	7	5	5	13	70
21	37	—	—	—	5	95	5	—	2	2	91	—	6	10	13	71
22	24	4	—	—	—	96	—	—	4	—	96	—	4	4	4	88
23	26	—	—	—	—	100	—	—	—	—	100	—	—	—	—	100
Total	229															

* After Table 39, page 115, McKern and Stewart, 1957.

Though the epiphysis for the medial border lags in the early twenties, fusion for all three is completed by 23 years of age.

Sternum

Morphologically, the sternum is the most variable bone in the body, and although there are 17 joint areas to provide age indications, their progression with age is not sufficiently uniform to be of real use in aging skeletal remains. On the basis of observed trends, however, some generalizations can be made.

Fusion of the component elements of the corpus sterni was observed to be essentially complete in most cases by 22-23 years (Tables XV and XVI) and, although rare, the uppermost segment was found still separate as late as 27 years.

TABLE XV*

Progress of Fusion Between Second and Third Segments of the Corpus Sterni—at Level of Attachment of Fourth Ribs (in %)

Age	No.	No Fusion	Beginning Fusion	Active Fusion	Recent Fusion	Complete Fusion
17-18	44	9.1	9.1	9.1	68.2	4.5
19	42	11.9	—	4.8	69.0	14.3
20	36	5.6	—	—	55.6	38.9
21	37	8.1	2.7	2.7	48.6	37.8
22	22	4.5	—	—	45.4	50.0
23	24	—	—	—	50.0	50.0
24-25	24	—	—	—	8.3	91.7

* After Table 41, page 123, McKern and Stewart, 1957.

TABLE XVI*

Progress of Fusion Between First and Second Segments of The Corpus Sterni—at Level of Attachment of Third Ribs (in %)

Age	No.	No Fusion	Beginning Fusion	Active Fusion	Recent Fusion	Complete Fusion
17-18	46	45.6	2.2	13.0	34.8	4.3
19	43	27.9	—	13.9	51.2	7.0
20	38	13.2	5.3	7.9	52.6	21.0
21	38	13.2	—	7.9	52.6	26.3
22	23	8.7	—	4.3	56.5	30.4
23	24	16.7	—	—	58.3	25.0
24-25	24	—	—	4.2	41.7	54.2
26-27	25	12.0	—	—	36.0	52.0
28-30	29	3.4	—	—	37.9	58.6

* After Table 42, page 123, McKern and Stewart, 1957.

The epiphyseal plate for the surface of the clavicular notch, although rather inconspicuous, was recorded as uniting between 18 and 22 years, with the greatest activity occurring at 19 years (Table XVII).

TABLE XVII*

Progress of Maturation of The Clavicular Notch (in %)

Age	No.	Epiphysis Ununited	Epiphysis Uniting	Surface Essentially Mature
17	9	33.3	—	66.7
18	35	2.8	5.7	91.4
19	43	—	9.3	90.7
20	42	—	4.8	95.2
21	36	—	2.8	97.2
22	19	—	5.3	94.7
23	23	—	—	100.0

* After Table 44, page 133, McKern and Stewart, 1957.

Sacrum

The several elements that comprise the sacrum begin to fuse from below, then upwards and along the sides. By 23 years, ossification is complete except between the S1-2 centra, where a gap may persist until as late as 32 years of age (Table XVIII).

TABLE XVIII*

**Age Distribution for Stages of Union Between
The Segments of The Sacrum (in %)**

Age	No.	S4-5 Stages					S3-4 Stages					S2-3 Stages					S1-2 Stages				
		0	1	2	3	4	0	1	2	3	4	0	1	2	3	4	0	1	2	3	4
17-18	55	7	5	7	22	47	8	6	14	48	24			25	45	30	1	3	23	70	3
19	52		2	4	29	65	2		7	40	51			11	28	61		4	9	81	6
20	45				26	74				21	79			9	27	64		2	9	67	22
21	39				14	86			2	18	80			5	27	68		2	8	66	24
22	24				8	92				12	88				20	80			4	63	33
23	26					100					100				8	92				63	37
24	14															100				35	65
25	13																			30	70
26-27	25																			55	45
28-29	19																			56	44
30-32	27																			37	63
33+	34																				100
Total	373																				

* After Table 48, page 148, McKern and Stewart, 1957.

Ribs

The data indicate a probable age of 17 years for first appearance of complete union of the head epiphyses, and a definite age of 23 years as the stage when all ribs are mature in all cases (Table XIX). Ossification begins in the upper and lower ribs, and slowly progresses towards the middle. Thus, the last ribs to become fully ossified are ribs 4 through 9.

TABLE XIX*

Rib Head Epiphyses: Age Distribution of The Percentage of Complete Union

Age	No.	Ribs											
		1	2	3	4	5	6	7	8	9	10	11	12
17	10	—	—	—	—	—	—	—	—	—	—	—	—
18	45	40	24	17	15	15	11	13	15	20	22	22	38
19	52	41	30	25	19	17	17	11	13	15	21	30	36
20	45	64	55	52	46	46	31	28	28	31	38	53	60
21	37	78	73	70	64	67	64	54	51	62	67	73	78
22	25	96	92	86	80	84	84	72	72	80	86	92	92
23	27	96	96	96	92	92	92	92	92	92	96	96	96
24	14	100	100	100	100	100	100	100	100	100	100	100	100
Total	255												

* After Table 50, page 158, McKern and Stewart, 1957.

We had expected variability, but not to the extent observed. Probably the most recent and detailed demonstration of the variability of epiphyseal union has been reported by Stewart (1969, figure 60). His data come mainly from the same Korean war-dead sample, but his portrayal of the variability is more highly explicit. For many years, for example, experts placed the complete union of the head of the humerus between 19.5 and 20.5 years. Stewart found that union at this site can occur at any time between 16 (?) and 23 years of age. Such disparity was found to exist at all epiphyseal sites.

Suture Closure

Generally, suture closure seems to progress in a fairly uniform manner; however, although the sutures and their patterns of closure are related to each other, this

TABLE XX*
**A Simplified Presentation of The Stages
of Suture Closure to Show its Variability: Vault Sutures (in %)**

Age	No.	Sagittal Closures**				Lambdoid Closures**				Coronal Closures**			
		0	1	2,3	4	0	1	2,3	4	0	1	2,3	4
17-18	55	75	4	12	9	92	—	5	3	99	—	—	1
19	52	66	4	10	19	83	5	5	7	84	7	5	4
20	45	54	10	13	23	82	11	3	4	77	17	2	4
21	37	56	9	10	25	72	10	10	8	86	7	2	5
22	24	54	17	5	24	75	17	4	4	72	20	4	4
23	26	42	11	15	32	65	6	23	6	49	34	11	6
24-25	27	34	7	11	48	53	11	18	18	67	12	14	7
26-27	25	12	8	40	40	32	28	16	24	28	16	24	32
28-30	29	18	12	19	51	27	17	35	21	26	25	25	24
31-40	43	10	4	14	72	24	17	20	39	20	20	35	25
41-50	6	2	16	66	16	1	66	—	33	50	33	—	16
Total	369												

* After Table 8, page 28, McKern and Stewart, 1957.

** 0: No closure anywhere 　　　　　　 2,3: No more than Stages 2 or 3
　　 1: No more than Stage 1 anywhere 　　 4: Stage 4 in some part

TABLE XXI*
**Total Suture Score for Ages 17-39 Showing Age Range, Mean Age, and
Predicted Age Based on The Regression of Suture Closure and Age**

Score	Age Range	Mean Age	Predicted Age From Regression
15	17-38	22.5	20.2
16	18-25	22.3	20.6
17	18-36	25.5	21.2
18	17-23	19.5	21.7
19	17-37	21.4	22.2
20	18-38	24.7	22.7
21	18-34	23.5	23.2
22	17-34	23.7	23.7
23	19-39	26.6	24.2
24	18-31	23.7	24.7
25	18-36	23.5	25.2
26	19-39	28.3	25.7
27	21-27	24.2	26.2
28	17-39	28.2	26.7
29	20-32	26.5	27.2
30	30-33	31.5	27.7
31	20-33	26.0	28.2
32	30-35	32.5	28.7
33	31-33	32.5	29.2
34	26-38	32.5	29.7

N = 356

Scores:	Age:	r = .4910
Mean: 21.71	Mean: 23.58	Predicted age: 0.5026 Scores + 12.6655
S. D.: 5.00	S. D.: 5.12	Standard error of estimate: 4.4614

* After Table 16, page 36, McKern and Stewart, 1957.

relationship is not sufficiently close to be applied reliably in cases of individual age determination (see Table XX). The effect of variability in suture closure can be slightly offset by basing age estimates on total suture closure, and such estimates have demonstrated a greater accuracy than those based on the closure pattern of a single suture. Table XXI demonstrates how a simple score can give a predicted age that is based upon the regression of total suture closure and age. Details of this procedure may be found in the previously noted report (McKern and Stewart, 1957, p. 35).

An exception to the general variability of suture closure is the spheno-occipital synchondrosis, or "basilar suture." Table XXII shows active fusion between 17 and 18 years; closure is completed at the age of 21 years.

Our analysis of suture closure illustrates the fact that the progress of closure has only a very general relationship with age. Thus, suture closure, with the exception of the spheno-occipital, is generally unreliable as evidence for skeletal age determination.

TABLE XXII*
The Age Distribution of Stages of Closure
in The Basilar Suture (in %)

Age	No.	Closure				
		0	1	2	3	4
17-18	55	3	2	7	10	78
19	52	—	—	—	3	97
20	45	—	—	—	2	98
21	37	—	—	—	—	100
22	24	—	—	—	—	100

* After Table 15, page 35, McKern and Stewart, 1957.

Skeletal Age Estimated from Combined Maturation

Because of the gross variability found in the maturative progress among skeletal growth areas, age estimates that are based upon single biological events may be seriously misleading. Where complete skeletons have been judged heretofore, it has been customary to base the final age assessments upon the combined growth status of as many areas as possible. It has been demonstrated, however, that, rather than emphasize complete skeletal coverage, reliable age estimates can better be derived from the combined maturational activity of a small number of critical growth areas (McKern and Stewart, 1957; McKern, 1957). In other words, the age status of a given skeleton can be predicted from the sum of the scores for the epiphyseal activity in the following *critical* areas:

Medial end of clavicle	Medial epicondyle, humerus
Iliac crest	Distal end, radius
Distal end, femur	Lateral joints, sacrum
Head, femur	3-4 joint, sacrum
Head, humerus	

The status of maturational progress for each area is scored on a 1-5 scale:

1 = non-union	4 = three-quarters united
2 = one-quarter union	5 = complete union
3 = half-union	

A total maturational score is then derived by adding the scores taken for the individual events. Total scores may be translated into a predicted age by reference to Table 18. Table XXIII has not been carried beyond 25 years of age because ossification is essentially complete by that time. Most of the epiphyses that still exhibit degrees of non-union at 25 years linger on for several years and terminate erratically.

TABLE XXIII*

Total Maturational Score for Skeletal Segment III Showing Age Range and Predicted Age Based on The Regression of Segmental Score and Age**

Total Score	Observed Age Range	Predicted Age
18	17-18	17.98
20	17-20	18.13
22	17-20	18.28
24	17-21	18.43
26	17-20	18.59
28	17-20	18.74
30	17-21	18.89
32	17-22	19.04
34	17-22	19.19
36	17-22	19.34
38	18-23	19.15
40	18-24	20.27
42	18-25	21.39
44	19-25	22.52
46	19-25	23.64

* Taken in part from Table 51, p. 166, McKern and Stewart, 1957.
** Age prediction equations:

(Scores 18-36)   Age = .0758 Score + 16.6146
(Scores 38-46)   Age = .5617 Score + 2.1995

For age estimates in the older age groups, it is still necessary to depend upon the maturation status of such individual events as the symphyseal surface of the pubic bone, or the medial epiphysis of the clavicle.

Age determination from combined maturation is time-consuming. It assumes, furthermore, the availability·of a more or less complete skeleton. It was desirable, therefore, to find a single factor that might reliably and consistently be used for age estimations.

It is generally known that the symphyseal face of the pubic bone undergoes a number of easily recognizable changes during the lifetime of an individual, especially between the ages of 16 and 50 years. Morphological changes in the pubic symphysis have been described by many, but it was T. W. Todd (1920) who first established age categories based upon these changes. Again, however, Todd's skeletal sample did not offer adequate age documentation, and his age categories had to be suspect. Now, with the excellent documentation provided by the Korean war-dead series, a re-evaluation of symphyseal changes as they relate to skeletal age has been possible, and the hope is that they will produce a more accurate tool for age estimates.

The Pubic Symphysis

Maturation of the pubic bone's symphyseal surface is marked by a succession of changes that extend into the latter decades of adult life. These changes are characterized by the obliteration of surface ridges, the formation of a dorsal plateau, the build up of a ventral rampart, and the eventual breakdown of surface structure along with erratic ossification of the symphyseal margins.

In an attempt to remedy the many problems that faced Todd, we used a somewhat different approach. Our method is based on the maturative progress of three independent and easily recognized components of the symphyseal surface:

Component I. Dorsal Plateau. In the early age groups (up to 17-18 years), the symphyseal surface is covered by a pattern of transverse ridges and grooves. With progressing age, a delimiting dorsal margin appears that eventually outlines the entire dorsal half of the surface. Then, through the interacting processes of resorption and fill-in, the ridge-groove pattern becomes obliterated, to give the resulting surface a flat, platform-like aspect.

Component II. Ventral Rampart. Early in the development of Component I, the ventral half of the symphyseal face has a porous appearance and is beveled. Over this beveled surface an epiphysis, or rampart, forms as an in-growth from its upper and lower extremities. This pattern is variable, however, and the rampart may remain incomplete. Such cases are characterized in the older age groups by a depression in the middle two-thirds of the ventral border.

Component III. Symphyseal Rim. After Component I and Component II have nearly completed their development, and the symphyseal articular face is more or less level in character, there next is formed a distinct and elevated rim which ultimately surrounds the entire face. At the same time, the bony texture of the face undergoes a transformation from granular to finely grained and smooth. Following the completion of the symphyseal rim, there is a period during which changes are minute and infrequent. Ultimately, the rim is worn down, and the resulting smooth surface extends to the margins of the face. In addition, as the face levels off it undergoes erosion and erratic ossification, and lipping may occur along the margins.

Since the metamorphosis of Components I and II is confined to the dorsal and ventral halves of the symphyseal face, respectively, the term "demi-face" (dorsal and ventral) has been introduced when referring to these Components (see Figure 8). Descriptions of the developmental stages for each of the Components are as follows:

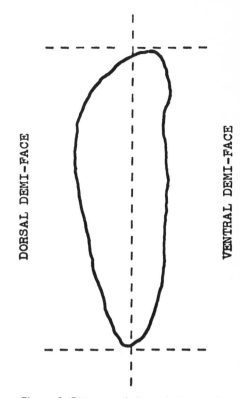

Figure 8. Diagram of the articular surface on the left side of a male pubic symphysis divided into dorsal and ventral demi-faces.

Component I—Dorsal Plateau:

Stage 0 : A dorsal margin is absent

Stage 1 : A slight margin formation first appears in the middle third of the dorsal border.

Stage 2 : The dorsal margin extends along the entire dorsal border.

Stage 3 : A filling in of grooves and a resorption of the ridges begins to form a beginning plateau in the middle third of the dorsal demi-face.

Stage 4 : The plateau, still exhibiting vestiges of billowing, extends over most of the dorsal demi-face.

Stage 5 : The billowing disappears completely, and the surface of the entire demi-face becomes flat and slightly granulated in texture.

Component II—Ventral Rampart:

Stage 0 : The ventral beveling is absent.

Stage ·1 : The ventral beveling is present only at the superior extremity of the ventral border.

Stage 2 : The bevel extends inferiorly along the ventral border.

Stage 3 : The ventral rampart begins by means of bony extensions from either, or both, extremities.

Stage 4 : The rampart is extensive, but gaps are still evident along the earlier ventral border, most obviously in the upper two-thirds.

Stage 5 : The rampart is complete.

Component III—Symphyseal Rim:

Stage 0 : The symphyseal rim is absent.

Stage 1 : A partial dorsal rim is present, usually at the superior end of the dorsal margin. It is round and smooth in texture and elevated above the symphyseal face.

Stage 2 : The dorsal rim is complete, and the ventral rim is beginning to form. There is no absolute site at which formation begins.

Stage 3 : The symphyseal rim is complete. The enclosed symphyseal surface is finely grained in texture and irregular, or undulating, in appearance.

Stage 4 : The rim begins to break down. The face becomes smooth and flat, and the rim is no longer round, but sharply defined. There is some evidence of lipping on the ventral edge.

Stage 5 : A further breakdown of the rim, especially along the superior ventral edge, and with rarefaction of the symphyseal face. There is also disintegration and erratic ossification along the ventral rim.

To arrive at an age estimate, each of the three Components is scored by associating the appropriate Component stage with that of the symphysis to be identified. These three scores are then added, and the predicted age for that sum can be read from Table XXIV.

TABLE XXIV*
Calculated Mean Age, Standard Deviation and Age Ranges for The Total Scores of The Symphyseal Formulae

Total Score	No.	Age Range for the Scores	Mean Age	Standard Deviation
0	7	-17	17.29	.49
1-2	76	17-20	19.04	.79
3	43	18-21	19.79	.85
4-5	51	18-23	20.84	1.13
6-7	26	20-24	22.42	.99
8-9	36	22-28	24.14	1.93
10	19	23-28	26.05	1.87
11-12-13	56	23-39	29.18	3.33
14	31	29 +	35.84	3.89
15	4	36 +	41.00	6.22
Total	349			

* After Table 27, page 85, McKern and Stewart, 1957.

To facilitate field use of the symphyseal formula, as well as its proper use as a training aid, sets of plastic model symphyseal casts, which represent the three Components and their five developmental stages, have been fabricated and marketed (Figure 9).* Estimates of skeletal age may be achieved by matching the various Component stages that are represented in the plastic set with the unknown pubic bone. Scoring and a final age assessment may be reached by following the procedure just outlined.

Obviously, we still have variability. But it is better controlled. In testing the reliability of this technique, we found that, given a complete skeleton and using only the pubic symphysis, age estimates based upon this single event will produce better results than estimates taken from any combination of epiphyseal sites. This technique has made age estimation for unknown skeletal remains more realistic, more accurate, and more dependable.

* Available through Darrell Van Buren, Inc., 81 Diamond Street, Walpole, Massachusetts 02081.

Figure 9. Set of plastic casts of pubic bones representing the three components of symphyseal metamorphosis and their five stages (from McKern and Stewart, 1957, Fig. 43.).

Concluding Statement

There is no denying the fact that a remarkable orderliness exists in the progress of skeletal maturation. Our principal conclusion, however, must be that individual maturational features, or events, are highly variable in a chronological sense, and that the present documentation of this full variability, including the emphasis we have placed thereon, represents a step forward in identification procedures.

Our concern with the problem of variability in maturation stems, of course, from the very nature of human identification. As a rule, the identification specialist has no way of knowing what is the racial, sociological, or health status of the individual he is dealing with. Any, or all, of these factors could have affected—accelerated or retarded—the unknown's rate of growth. All that the specialist can predict with safety is the age range in which the observed complex of maturational features are known to occur. If he attempts to place the individual in a particular spot in the age range, he is only guessing—and he must admit it. The present evidence for variability should induce caution.

What of future research in the area of age identification? It would seem that we have done fairly well in our understanding of age changes in the human male skeleton. Our most frustrating problem concerns the same information relative to female skeletal growth, and the recognition of those critical changes which would aid in the estimation of female skeletal age. We do know that, although we are dealing with the same skeletal areas, the age indicators for females are not similar. It has become increasingly apparent that, in mass disasters, females comprise an increasingly greater majority of victims—other than in the case of war. Certainly there is an immediate need for additional research into female skeletal maturation. The author and others are now working on the problem, the primary obstacle to completion being the scarcity of documented female samples.

This paper may have left the reader with a feeling of pessimism concerning our abilities to specify the age of unknown skeletal remains. This was not intentional. It should be emphasized that our new knowledge of the true nature of skeletal maturation, and its great variability, can now produce age estimates that are much more realistic. With this knowledge, we are better scientists. We become better consultants. We admit that we do not have all the answers. But, based upon our present knowledge, we do know the areas for future research where educated guesses can then become anatomical fact.

Literature Cited

Krogman, W. M.
　　1939. A Guide to the Identification of Human Skeletal Material. *FBI Law Enforcement Bulletin,* 8:1-29.

McKern, T. W.
　　1957. Estimation of Skeletal Age from Combined Maturational Activity. *American Journal of Physical Anthropology,* 15:399-408.

McKern, T. W., and Stewart, T. D.
　　1957. Skeletal Age Changes in Young American Males, Analyzed from the Standpoint of Age Identification. *Technical Report EP-45,* Environmental Protection Research Division, Quartermaster Research and Development Center, U.S. Army, Natick, Mass.

Stewart, T. D.
　　1963. New Developments in Evaluating Evidence from the Skeleton. *Journal of Dental Research,* 42 (1) part 2:264-73.
　　1969. Identification by Skeletal Structures. Chapter 11 (pages 123-54) in *Gradwohl's Legal Medicine,* edited by Francis E. Camps. 2d edition, John Wright & Sons Ltd., Bristol, England.

Todd, T. W.
　　1920. Age Changes in the Pubic Bone. I. The Male White Pubic. *American Journal of Physical Anthropology,* 3:285-334.

Estimation of Skeletal Age: After About Age 30

Ellis R. Kerley

The estimation of age from skeletal features alone is more difficult in the remains of mature adults than in those of children, adolescents, and young adults. In the latter, skeletal age manifests itself through the sequence of maturation at the many sites where growth takes place, and eventually, in the third decade, shows up in the form of a complete cessation of growth. Thereafter, skeletal age changes are mainly degenerative in character, tend to be widespread, and often are rather sensitive to physiological changes that result from such things as malnutrition and disease. This being the case, it becomes especially important to work toward a refinement of all the means for estimating age in mature skeletons. Progress along this line has been remarkable in recent years and, therefore, the purpose of this paper is to review the existing state of the available procedures.

The Skull

Suture Closure. T. Wingate Todd and D. W. Lyon, Jr. (1924–25) described in detail the progressive fusion and obliteration of the cranial sutures, and the relationship of these processes with age in Whites and Negroes. However, only in connection with the endocranial closure of the sutures—a phase of the general process not readily observable in whole skulls—did these authors consider the applicability of their observations to the estimation of age in individual cases. Taking a random sample of 30 cases, they correctly estimated the age in only 3, overestimated the age (by from 1 to 23 years) in 13, and underestimated the age (by from 1 to 19 years) in 14. As a result, they concluded that ". . . it cannot be denied that so far our work does not justify the uncontrolled use of suture closure in estimation of age" (1924, p. 379).

In spite of this restriction, Krogman (1939) assigned fairly exact ages to the phases of endocranial suture closure with no qualification. For example (p. 12):

Suture	Begin	Rapid	Final
Sagittal	22	26-31	35
Coronal	24	26-29	38-42
Lambdoid	26	26-29	42-47

He stated, moreover, that although ectocranial closure is more variable than endocranial, the two take place concurrently. Perhaps because Krogman cited no sources for this information, and because his Identification Guide was published by the FBI, anthropologists and identification experts alike accepted and applied the data without question for some 15 years. In recent years, Singer (1953) was the first of several to question the reliability of suture closure for aging purposes (see also McKern in this volume). As a result, few people active in skeletal identification

Figure 10. Superior aspect of a skull that shows bilateral thinning of the parietal bones in old age.

today use cranial suture closure as more than a general indication of age, or as other than a last resort when better means are not available because of the incompleteness of the remains. Although this is progress only in the sense of correcting an existing misconception, it deserves a place in this review.

Parietal Thinning. Occasionally, the skull of an undoubtedly old individual shows symmetrical depressions in the regions of the parietal bosses, Figure 10. The depressions are the result of a thinning of the skull wall in such a way that the outer table comes closer to the inner table with advancing age. Although the cause is not well understood, the result has been described as senile osteoporosis of the parietals. When present, the abnormality can be taken as a reliable indicator of advanced age; that is, an age not likely under 60 and probably older. On the other hand, of course, its absence is no indication of an age under 60, since the condition is rare in the United States at any age.

Cumulative Changes in the Teeth. As compared with the skull vault which, as we have seen, yields only general indications of age, the permanent teeth, when present, permit much closer aging. Some of the dental features that best reflect age can be judged grossly; others must be viewed microscopically. Since some of these features pertain to the crown, and others to the root, isolated whole teeth give the best results. Also, the reliability of the age estimates depends to a great extent upon the experience of the observer, especially in reading the thin longitudinal sections. Anthropologists and forensic pathologists, therefore, should defer to forensic dentists on this score. When this is done, and the analysis takes the form recommended by Gustafson (1950) or one of the more recent modifications (for example, that of Miles, 1963), the estimates have a claimed average accuracy of plus or minus 3.6 years or better.

The Rest of the Skeleton

Ossification of rib cartilages. Man, like the other primates, lacks sternal ribs (Stewart, 1961) and, instead, has cartilages of varying length in the area of the thoracic wall between the anterior ends of the vertebral ribs and the sternum. The place where each vertebral rib joins its cartilage is known as the costochrondral junction. The joint thus formed is known as a synarthrosis. In adolescents, the joint surfaces present a billowed appearance, and with rounded margins where the cartilage and periosteum meet. Then, in young and middle-aged adults, the margins of the rib ends are seen to become progressively sharper as the periosteum extends bone onto the surface of the cartilage. This means that the rib ends become more and more cup-shaped. Also, since this late stage of bone formation is somewhat irregular, the rib ends tend to take on a ragged appearance and, in some cases, to exhibit bone extending well out into what was costal cartilage in youth, Figure 11.

Figure 11. Three views of the ventral ends of ribs to show progressive age changes. A, at age 16; B, at age 34; and C, at age 72.

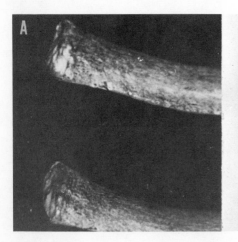
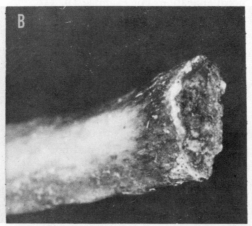
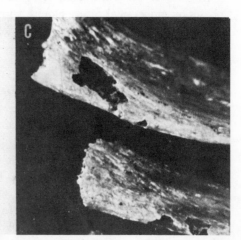

Occasionally, unossified islands of cartilage are left as small, isolated balls scattered through the ossified portion of the cartilage that is beyond the old costochondral junction. But in advanced age complete ossification of the costal cartilage is not uncommonly seen. Thus, the radiological picture ranges from small discrete islands of bone along the course of the cartilage, Figure 12, to more or less solid bone extending from the original vertebral rib end to the sternum. Microscopically, the picture is that of regular cancellous bone, with marrow in the spaces between the trabeculae.

On the other hand, most of these calcified or ossified cartilages are usually lost when the remains are skeletonized. McKern and Stewart (1957) may have realized this, or considered their soldier subjects too young to show anything but the earliest stage of costal-cartilage ossification. Thus, although they did not include this specific feature in their analysis, they did illustrate various degrees of ossification of first rib cartilage (sometimes more firmly attached to the manubrium than to the rib). The examples they picture, Figures 74 and 75, range in age from 25 to 38 years, with the two most extreme being 32 and 38 years of age. Apparently, therefore, the first rib can show this change quite early, and more evidence of the same sort, at other sites, is needed to indicate ages beyond 40. Much more work needs to be done on this subject, however, and especially on the role of trauma in inducing ossification of the costal cartilages.

Lipping of the Vertebral Centra. A joint structure, similar to that between the ribs and sternum, likewise exists between the segments of the vertebral column. Here, the intervertebral disk corresponds to the costal cartilage. The resemblance ends at this point because, among other things, the intervertebral disk, unlike the costal cartilage, is designed for weight bearing and does not normally ossify. Instead, osteophytic outgrowths, from the anterior and lateral margins of the centra, begin to appear at the levels where joint motion is greatest. Stewart (1958) combined his observations on the remains of American soldiers with those on the older skeletons in the Terry Collection from the dissecting room of Washington University, St. Louis; and he showed that the osteophytes rarely become prominent before 40 years of age in males, Figure 13. He believed it was impossible to go further than this in estimating age from such evidence.

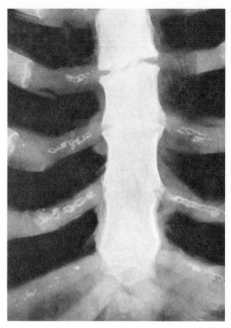

Figure 12. Radiograph showing calcification of the costal cartilages in old age.

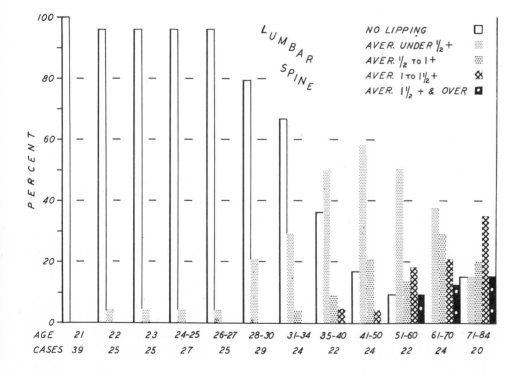

Figure 13. Graph showing the distribution of five categories of osteophytosis in 306 lumbar spines of White American males who ranged in age from 21 to 84 years (from Stewart, 1958, Fig. 1.).

A further word of caution is needed here. The osteophytes that develop naturally with aging must be distinguished from the much more extensive pathological ossification seen in Marie-Strümpel's ankylosing spondylitis. As the name implies, this disease, which begins in young adulthood and is largely confined to males, results in the fusion of the spinal and sacroiliac joints.

Metamorphosis of the Pubic Symphysis. A third joint of the synarthrodial class that yields evidence of age is the pubic symphysis. Because of its location in the anterior midline of the pelvis, between the two pubic bones, this joint bears no weight and is therefore more like the costochondral joints than the intervertebral joints. Yet it presents a much larger surface than any of the costochondral joints, is of a less delicate bony structure, and offers more surface detail for use in estimating age.

Here again, T. Wingate Todd must be remembered for his pioneer aging studies (1920-21). One of his contributions was to identify 10 stages of pubic joint metamorphosis. To each of these stages he assigned an age range. Thus by comparing the symphyseal surface of an unknown with the descriptions of Todd's stages, and by establishing in this way the best match, it is possible to arrive at an age estimate. This process was simplified after 1938 when photographs of Todd's modal stages were reduced to drawings. Krogman did not use these drawings in his 1939 identification guide, and there is uncertainty as to whether they were published prior to 1954 when they appeared in Stewart's chapter in the first edition of Gradwohl's *Legal Medicine*. Sometime during World War II, however, photographic copies of the drawings were being passed around from hand to hand, and so they eventually became widely known and used.

Stewart's observations on the war dead (see McKern's chapter in this volume) provided extensive data for an age period (20-40) that was poorly represented in the material available to Todd. The resulting modification of Todd's method has two advantages:

1. Comparisons of specimens is facilitated by the substitution of casts of the pubic bones for the drawings previously used
2. Probable errors of estimate are more accurate.

Note, however, that the modified method does not apply to older individuals, nor to females.

Changes in the Diarthrodial Joints. Most of the other joints of the skeleton are diarthroses and differ from the preceding in having the cartilage-covered bony elements separated by an articular cavity within a capsule. In all such joints there is a tendency for the bone-cartilage junction to continue ossifying throughout life. In youth, the peri-articular margins of joints of this class are smooth and continuous, but in old age these margins may develop an elevated ridge, or cuff, of bone. Johnson (1962) has shown that these peri-articular ridges result from the progressive remodeling of the subchondral plate. Although bony outgrowths of this sort indicate advancing age, they have not proved useful for estimating exact age. Also, one must not be misled by excessive changes in one, or a few, neighboring joints that are the result of localized trauma.

Resorption of Cancellous Bone. The gross structure of the interior of the long bones provides additional clues as to age. So far, the only useful studies of this nature deal with the proximal end of the humerus and the femur (Hansen, 1953-54; Schranz, 1959). The method has its greatest utility in connection with skeletonized remains. This is because the features under study are best seen in longitudinally sectioned macerated bones. Mainly involved is the determination of the arrangement of the cancellous tissue, which does not show up very well in X-rays.

In youth and young adulthood, the cancellous bone extends well down from the proximal epiphysis into the adjoining metaphyseal part of the diaphysis. As age advances, osteoclastic resorption gradually removes the more distal part of this cancellous bone in such a way as to produce a concavity proximal-wards. The effect is to enlarge the medullary cavity. Nonhematopoetic fatty marrow fills the vacated part of the medullary cavity. According to Schranz, in the humerus the upper cone-shaped end of the medullary cavity approaches, but does not quite reach, the level of the surgical neck during the age period 31-40. Then, during the age period 41-50, the cone reaches the level of the surgical neck. Not until the age period of 61-74 does it reach the epiphyseal line.

Although other changes in the cancellous bone also need to be taken into consideration in arriving at age estimates, the procedure at present does not support estimates that are closer than a decade.

Cumulative Changes in the Cortex. It was pointed out above, in connection with the skull, that the closest estimates of age in mature individuals can be obtained by a microscopic examination of the teeth. The same holds true with regard to the rest of the skeleton, especially when the results of a gross examination of the features previously mentioned are compared with a microscopic examination of the cortex of the major long bones of the leg. Although the cumulative microscopic age changes in the cortex can be seen in most of the tubular long bones of the skeleton, these changes have been correlated with chronologic age only for the femur, tibia, and fibula (Kerley, 1965, 1969).

With experience, rough estimates of the ages of these bones from any individual can be made by examining, at low magnification, the resorptive patterns in the cortex as they appear in cross-sections—from the middle of the diaphyses, either in the form of thin slides or simply the opaque specimens themselves. In actual practice, even without magnification, it is usually possible to see the areas of intense resorptive activity in the cross-sections of major long bones, but the distinction between normal and abnormal bone resorption—an important consideration in such work—depends upon having a closer look at the lining of the resorption cavities.

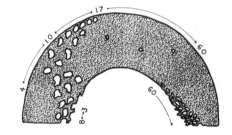

Figure 14 gives a general idea of the normal age progression of the cortical changes, credit for some of which is due primarily to the work of Amprino and Bairati (1936) and Jowsey (1960). From birth through about 3 years of age, the most intense resorptive activity is located in the medullary third of the cortex. From around 4 until nearly 11 years of age, the resorptive activity is intense and evenly distributed throughout the cortex. From about 10 years of age until almost 17, there is intense cortical resorption, with most of the activity located around the periphery, just under the periosteal surface of the bone. After age 17, the massive resorption in the outer third of the cortex ceases and the microscopic texture remains thick and homogeneous. This period of seeming quiescence is explained by the close matching in the rates of osteoclastic resorption and osteoblastic replacement.

Figure 14. Diagram of the cortex of a long bone to show the shift with age in the areas where maximum resorptive activity occurs.

Activity reappears much later, and then the inner third of the cortex is progressively resorbed. The range of variation in females—with regard to the age of onset of this late medullary resorption—is very wide and may begin as early as 40. In males, this range is only moderately wide and does not usually begin until around 40. The medullary resorption of old age can be distinguished from the form seen in infancy by the different sizes of the bones.

Although these shifts—in the patterns of cortical resorption with age—lack the age specificity necessary for accurate estimates of individual ages, they are useful in sorting commingled bone fragments when the individuals involved are of different ages. Beyond this, closer age estimates by this means require microscopic examination of the cortex. A method utilizing this approach has been described by the writer (Kerley, 1965, 1969) and will be summarized here, along with the results of practical applications, and with such modifications of the original technique that experience now indicates may be warranted.

To establish the basis for a reliable system of age estimation from microscopic bone structure, a series of bone cross-sections from individuals of known age had to be assembled. The bones selected for study were the femur, tibia, and fibula, the largest bones of the leg. The sections came from the midshafts. Eventually 126 individuals, ranging in age from birth to 95 years, were sampled. Half were over age 35, the period of life which gives the most difficulty in age estimation by the gross methods. Both sexes were represented, as were three racial stocks: Caucasoid, Negroid, and Mongoloid. Also, it is important to note that all of the sections used to establish age-range curves were either from individuals free from bone disease, or from individuals whose pathologic condition did not involve the part of the leg sampled.

Thin ground sections were made from the collected specimens and mounted as histologic slides. Under high magnification these showed that, although much the same changes occur at different ages in all parts of a cortical cross-section, the outer third of the cortex usually exhibits the greatest uniformity in bone texture throughout the entire age span. Except for the brief period of adolescence, this area is least affected by the resorptive changes previously described. For this reason, all of the microscopic features used by the writer to establish age-range curves were observed in the outer third of the cross-section. To compensate for possible variations in the texture of different parts of this cortical zone, however, four widely separated points were selected for 100-power viewing and study. These points were picked to represent the anterior, posterior, medial, and lateral sides of the cross-sections. Also, at each of these points the selected microscopic field just touched the outer edge of the cross-section, the field being a circular area 1.25 mm in diameter as formed by 10× ocular wide-field lenses and a 10 × objective lens.

When considered in detail at the microscopic level, the resorptive change in the cortex already referred to can be separated into four main structural components that are present at any time. These are:

1. Whole osteons
2. Fragments of osteons
3. Circumferential lamellar bone
4. Non-Haversian canals.

Components 1, 2 and 4 were reported as the total number estimated to be present in all four fields; component 3 was reported as the average percent of all four fields filled with this type of bone. Each of these four cortical components will now be described with reference to Figure 15, a typical microscopic picture of the outer

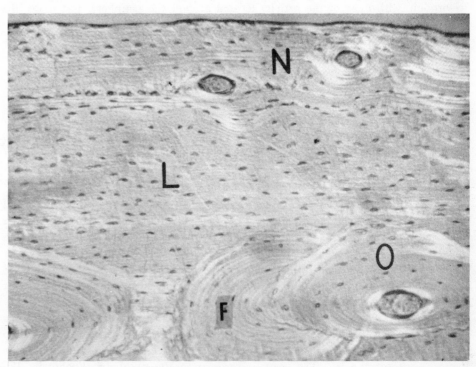

Figure 15. Photomicrograph of the outer zone of the cortex in a long bone from a young adult. The four structural components used to estimate age are identified as follows: O, osteon; F, osteon fragment; L, circumferential lamellar bone; and N, non-Haversian canal.

zone of the cortex at the early mature stage.

1. Osteons are tubular vascular channels which, in a long bone, run more or less parallel to the long axis. In cross-sections they appear as holes in the bone surrounded by concentric lamellae, and with evenly spaced osteocytes in their lacunae, or spaces. In the remodeling process, osteons begin as large spaces that subsequently fill from the periphery, inward, as lamellae are put down in successive concentric layers. A so-called "reversal line" of denser bone marks the outer limit of an osteon. This is the place where osteoblastic bone formation began and osteolclasic resorption ceased.

2. When osteoclasts tunnel new longitudinal vascular channels through cortical bone containing osteons, those osteons in the way of the remodeling process are destroyed or damaged. The fragments of old osteons that are left become surrounded, eventually, by new osteons. The number of such fragments increases with advancing age.

3. Bones increase in diameter during the period of growth. In bringing this about the periosteal osteoblasts deposit fine layers, or lamellae, like the rings of an onion, on the outside of the existing cortex. Thus, lamellar bone has a circumferential orientation and, in youthful specimens, appears under polarized light as unbroken birefringent rings. With increasing age, of course, the circumferential lamellar bone is replaced by osteons.

4. As the bone grows, the circumferential lamellar layers of the cortex incorporate numerous, small, longitudinally directed blood vessels from the periosteum. Within these resultant tubular channels (called non-Haversian canals to distinguish them from the canals developed in the remodeling process) concentric lamellae may form and, in time, come to resemble osteons, and they are then called primary osteons. Unlike the secondary osteons, however, the primary osteons lack a reversal line and fail to interrupt the circumferential lamellae which, instead, bend around them. Non-Haversian canals and primary osteons are plentiful in the bones of adolescents and young adults, but disappear during early middle age.

These four cortical components are not always as clear-cut as described here, and some rules are required to help to distinguish between an osteon and an osteon fragment. Osteons sometimes show encroachments on their borders by adjacent osteons, and the problem in such cases is how to decide whether or not to classify them as fragments. As an arbitrary working rule in this study, a recognizable osteon was counted as such if it had an intact canal and otherwise was judged to be 80% complete. In other words, any osteon that had discernible areas where it had been encroached upon by subsequent generations of osteons was considered a fragment.

The foregoing, brief explanation of the cortical components selected for study, and the rules developed for their classification, should now make it easy to understand the analysis of the results of this study that follows. Since the primary objective was to relate some form of quantification, for the four selected cortical components with age, separate graphs were developed for the age ranges of each component of each bone. Unfortunately, the size of the sample was too small to permit separate consideration of the two sexes or of the different racial stocks. Figures 16-18 that deal with the components of the femur, tibia, and fibula, respectively, show the resulting age-range curves. The numbers of osteons and osteon fragments in the areas counted show an increase with advancing age in all four bones, but are different for each bone. Necessarily, therefore, the percentages for the areas occupied by lamellar bone, and the number of counted non-Haversian canals, decrease with advancing age in all three bones, but again they are somewhat different for each.

Table XXV presents the data from the age-range curves in the form of regression formulae. These can be used to estimate the age of an unknown with a statistically determined amount of error when the cortical data for the unknown has been obtained in the same way. Using twice the standard error as the plus-or-minus

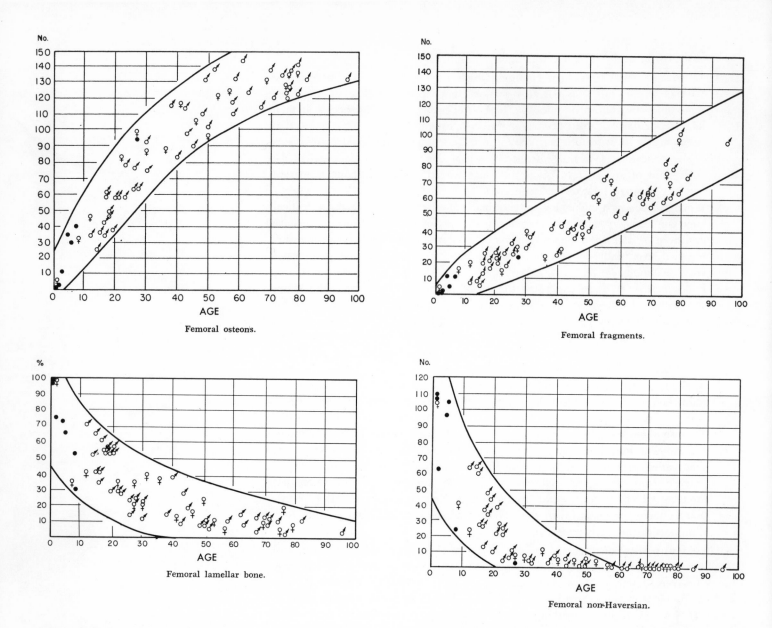

Femoral osteons.

Femoral fragments.

Femoral lamellar bone.

Femoral non-Haversian.

Figure 16. Age-range curves for the four cortical components of the femur (from Kerley, 1965, Fig. 4.).

limits for the error of the estimate, the age arrived at should fall within this error range in 95% of all cases. Since the osteon fragments of the fibula yielded the highest correlation with age (0.974), and hence the smallest standard error (5.27), 95% of the ages arrived at by means of the corresponding formula should not be in error by more than ±10.5 years. Other components in other bones yielded larger standard errors, which means that the plus-or-minus limits—within which 95% of the age estimates based thereon would be expected to fall—exceed 10.5 years. It is advisable, therefore—when presented with the skeleton of an unknown for age estimation—to select the regression formula to be used, in accordance with the available cortical data, so as to obtain the lowest standard error.

The reliability of age estimates from microscopic study of the cortex can be somewhat improved by combining the indications of all the cortical components for two or three different leg bones. For this purpose, the age-profile chart shown in Figure 19 was devised. In the case illustrated by this chart, all of the cortical components of the tibia and fibula were used. Those of the femur could have been used also, if it had been present. Starting with any one of the components, for example the tibial osteons, the procedure is as follows: By turning to the age-range curve for the tibia (Figure 17), the number of osteons counted in the four fields (of the outer third of the cortex) are located on the left side of the graph. One then follows horizontally

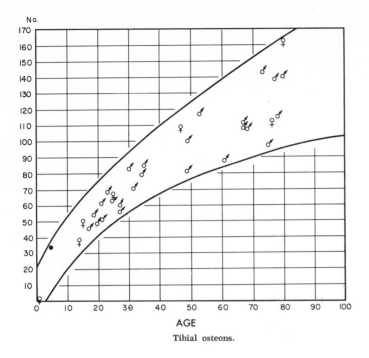

Tibial osteons.

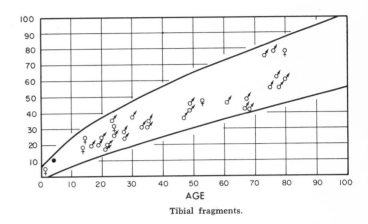

Tibial fragments.

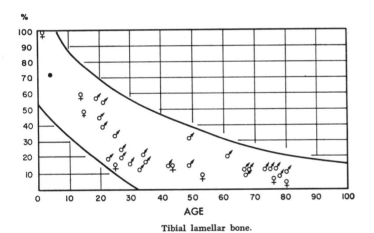

Tibial lamellar bone.

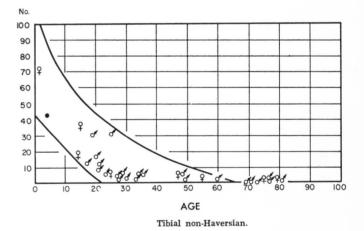

Tibial non-Haversian.

across the graph to the two points where the horizontal intersects the two sides of the age-range curve. By dropping verticals from these intersection points to the base line, the absolute age range for that number of osteons in the original sample is obtained; namely, 13 to 33 years. These figures are entered on the age-profile chart at the indicated place, and also in the form of a horizontal line that conforms with the given age scale. The same procedure is then repeated for each of the other three tibial components and for all four fibular components. Thereupon all 8 horizontal lines are connected by two vertical lines at a distance apart that is indicated by the highest *minimum* age and the lowest *maximum* age for all 8 ranges (respectively, 16 for fibular non-Haversian canals, and 30 for tibial non-Haversian canals). The distance between these vertical lines then represents the age range for which all cortical components of all available bones are in agreement. Estimated age in this case is the midpoint in the 16 to 30 year range, namely, 23 years.

At this point the reader must be cautioned about the construction of the vertical lines in the age-profile chart. If they show that the four cortical components in any given bone are in violent disagreement as to the age of the individual, or if all possible age ranges are excluded by a lack of overlapping ranges, the bone should be

Figure 17. Age-range curves for the four cortical components of the tibia (from Kerley, 1965, Fig. 5.).

rejected as unsuitable for age estimation and regarded as probably pathologic. On the other hand, if all components are in agreement for each bone, but there is a major inconsistency in the age ranges for two different bones, the possibility of commingling should be considered.

This method of estimating age by means of plotting an age-profile chart was tested on 56 additional cases that ranged in age from birth to 82 years. In all of these cases the estimates were within ±10 years of the actual ages. This finding suggested that the closeness of the estimate might differ between the two halves of the age range. Accordingly, when the series was divided into those 30 years of age and under, and those over 30 years of age, 91.7% of the estimates for the younger group, and 78.7% of the estimates for the older group, were within ±5 years of the actual ages.

Further evidence of the reliability of age estimates made in this way has accumulated through work on actual forensic cases. The details of 12 such cases are summarized in Table XXVI. In all of them, the estimated ages turned out to be within ±5 years of the actual ages at death. Considering that some of the skeletons were incomplete or badly fragmented, and that seven were from the age period beyond 30 years, when aging by traditional gross methods is little more than guesswork, these results are remarkable. Also, it is important to note that, in making the age estimates by this method, the sex and race of the individuals need not be known in advance.

Figure 18. Age-range curves for the four cortical components of the fibula (from Kerley, 1965, Fig. 6).

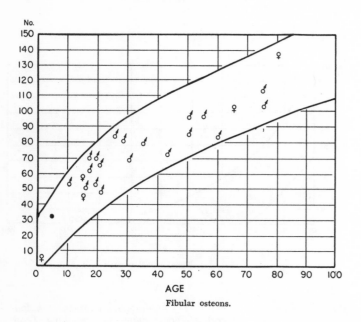

Fibular osteons.

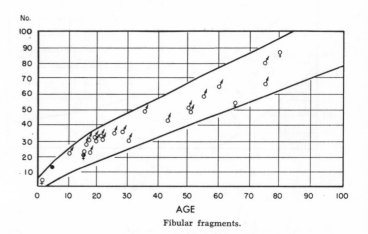

Fibular fragments.

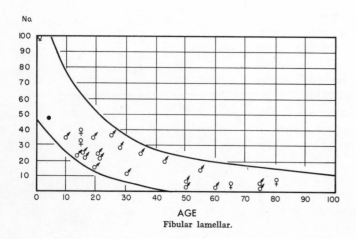

Fibular lamellar.

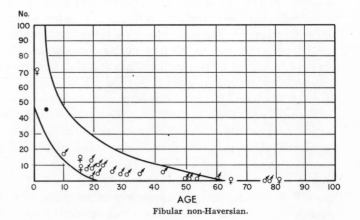

Fibular non-Haversian.

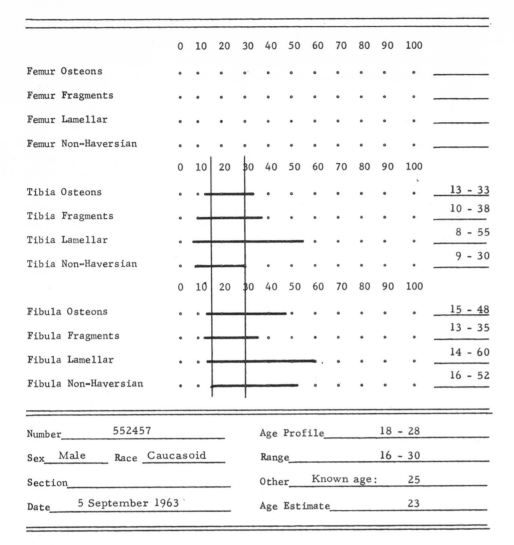

Figure 19. Age-profile chart to illustrate the age-range method of estimating age from four cortical components of the tibia and fibula of a male Caucasoid (from Kerley, 1965, Fig. 7).

Number _____ 552457 _____   Age Profile _____ 18 – 28 _____

Sex _Male_   Race _Caucasoid_   Range _____ 16 – 30 _____

Section _____   Other ___ Known age: 25 ___

Date _____ 5 September 1963 _____   Age Estimate _____ 23 _____

Up to this point little has been said about the effect of disease and postmortem bone deterioration on the age estimation by means of the microscopic study of cortical bone. Certain metabolic diseases can change the microscopic structure of the cortex, and even the rate of osteon turnover throughout the skeleton, but the presence of these abnormal conditions is usually readily detectable, either grossly or microscopically. Likewise, the presence of limited traumatized areas in the bones, including healing fractures, is obvious, and such areas can easily be avoided.

Among the postmortem changes that affect the cortex, and hence the aging method based thereon, are the natural deterioration of the bones, from exposure to the elements, and the charring or calcining that results from exposure to fire. Both of these processes may cause the outer part of the cortex to crack and flake off. Since the method depends upon the integrity of the outer third of the cortex, under these circumstances the loss of that area renders the specimen useless. When bodies are burned in the flesh, however, the muscles over some of the long bones, and particularly the femur, are often sufficiently thick to prevent parts of the shafts from being damaged beyond use.

Attention is also called to three interesting modifications of the present method, related solely to the femur, that are described by Ahlqvist and Damsten (1969). In the first place, these authors make the point that, since the cortical age changes consist of progressive replacement of lamellar bone, and its constituent non-Haversian canals by osteons and the accumulated fragments of old osteons, the best correlated, and most salient, features of this process can be represented simply by the combined numbers of osteons and osteon fragments expressed as a percentage, and as explained below. This point is well taken, especially since changing the procedure in this way obviates the need to distinguish between osteons and the fragments of old osteons.

In arriving at a percent expression for the osteons and osteon fragments present, Ahlqvist and Damsten resorted to the second modification of the original procedure. In place of a circular visual field, they used an ocular square-ruled network which was superimposed on the sections. The network, containing 100 squares, was inserted "into the eyepiece at such a level that, using a suitable magnification, the side of the square measures 1 mm at the level of the section" (p. 209). Then, by counting (under polarized light) the number of small squares that were more than half filled with osteons and osteon fragments, and then dividing the number of such small squares in all four fields by four, they obtained a figure that they refer to as "the percentage of bone covered by these structures" (p. 206).

The third modification has to do with the location of the points on the outer cortex where the observations are made. Ahlqvist and Damsten had observed that the femoral crest (*linea aspera*), which was used in the original procedure as the posterior point, has a highly variable distribution of osteons and osteon fragments, perhaps because it serves as an area for muscle attachment. They avoided the crest, therefore, and placed their points midway between the original ones. In their opinion, squares cover these areas better than circular fields.

Although these modifications, when taken together, represent a considerable saving of time and effort, and probably yield results with nearly the same level of reliability, they are applicable as yet only to the femur. For this purpose, the following linear regression applies: $y = 9.99x - 4.96 \pm 6.71$. In cases where time is an important consideration, or where the femur alone is available, the modified method should prove satisfactory.

Summary

For skeletons over 30 years of age, the age-estimating methods reviewed, and the relative reliability of the estimates, are summarized in Table XXVII. Depending mainly upon the condition of the remains, and particularly on the parts available for examination, the practical applicability of these methods will vary from one set of circumstances to another. In recent years research in this area has been active and undoubtedly will yield still more refined techniques as new approaches are explored. For the present, the methods discussed here, when used either singly or in combination, make it possible to estimate the age of mature skeletal remains with considerable accuracy, regardless of the age range represented or, within limits, the state of bone preservation.

TABLE XXV
Regression Formulae, Correlation Coefficients and Standard Errors for Four Cortical Components from the Outer Zone of the Femur, Tibia, and Fibula

Cortical component		Regression	Correlation	Standard error
		Femur		
Whole osteons	Y=	$3.473 + 0.144X + 0.003X^2$	$p=0.922$	9.39
Fragments of osteons	Y=	$8.786 + 0.834X$	$r=0.864$	12.19
Lamellar bone	Y=	$79.455 - 2.427X + 0.023X^2$	$p=0.870$	11.78
Non-Haversian canals	Y=	$57.811 - 1.728X + 0.013X^2$	$p=0.815$	13.85

TABLE XXV (continued)

Cortical component	Regression	Correlation	Standard error
	Tibia		
Whole osteons	$Y = -10.082 + 0.634X$	$r = 0.925$	6.69
Fragments of osteons	$Y = -7.061 + 0.931X + 2.210X^2 - 2.538X^3$	$p = 0.947$	7.78
Lamellar bone	$Y = 76.338 - 1.794X + 0.011X^2$	$p = 0.816$	13.62
Non-Haversian canals	$Y = 70.270 - 10.944X + 0.647X^2 - 0.011X^3$	$p = 0.790$	9.63
	Fibula		
Whole osteons	$Y = 2.366 - 0.538X + 0.018X^2 - 0.001X^3$	$p = 0.922$	8.83
Fragments of osteons	$Y = 1.328 - 0.058X + 0.034X^2$	$p = 0.974$	5.27
Lamellar bone	$Y = 69.108 - 2.208X + 0.015X^2$	$p = 0.881$	10.85
Non-Haversian canals	$Y = 55.241 - 4.300X + 0.050X^2$	$p = 0.879$	10.70

TABLE XXVI
Age-Estimate Reliability as Derived from the Microscopic Examination of the Cortex of Long Bones. Evidence from 12 Forensic Cases

Case number	Sex	Bones used	Estimated age	Actual Age
Aero-60-1	Male	Fibula	25-35 (30)	32
Aero-62-2	Male	Fibula	30-40 (35)	39
Aero-63-1	Male	Femur	34-44 (39)	43
FBI-63-1	Female	Femur	15-25 (20)	24
Aero-64-1	Male	Fibula	22-32 (27)	23
1151991	Female	Femur	27-37 (32)	33
Ky-65-1	Male	Tibia and fibula	24-34 (29)	25
Ky-65-2	Female	Femur	53-63 (58)	53
Ky-66-1	Male	Femur and fibula	56-66 (61)	65
ML-66-15	Male	Femur and tibia	71-81 (76)	81
KBI-68-1	Female	Femur	22-33 (28)	29
KBI-69-1	Female	Femur and fibula	13-23 (18)	18

TABLE XXVII
Summary of Available Methods for Estimating the Age of Adult Skeletons

Method	Practical age range	Skeletal part used	Type of accuracy	References
Suture closure	18-60	Skull	Generalized, unreliable	Todd & Lyon, 1924-25
Parietal osteoporosis	50+	Skull	Generalized, not uniform	Todd & Lyon, 1924-25
Rib end calcification	18+	Ribs	Generalized, progressive	Todd & Lyon, 1924-25
Vertebral osteophytosis	30+	Vertebrae	Generalized, progressive	Stewart, 1958
Lipping of joint margins	30+	Diarthrodial joints	Generalized, progressive	Johnson, 1962
Metamorphosis of pubic symphysis	18-50	Pubic symphysis	Documented, specific	McKern & Stewart, 1957
Microscopic dental remodeling	Birth-80	Teeth	Specific ±5 years	Gustafsson, 1950
Cancellous regression	20+	Femur, humerus	Documented, specific	Hansen, 1953-54; Schranz, 1959
Gross cortical resorption	Birth-95	Femur, tibia, fibula	General age periods	Kerley, 1969
Microscopic cortical remodeling	Birth-95	Femur, tibia, fibula	Specific, ±5 years	Kerley, 1965 and 1969; Ahlqvist & Damsten, 1969

Literature Cited

Ahlqvist, J., and Damsten, O.
  1969. A Modification of Kerley's Method for the Microscopic Determination of Age in Human Bone. *Journal of Forensic Sciences,* 14:205-12.
Amprino, R., and Bairati, A.
  1936. Processi di recostruzione e di riassorbimento nella sostanza compatta delle ossa dell'uomo. *Zeitschrift für Zellforschung und mikroskopische Anatomie,* 24:439-511.
Gustafson, G.
  1950. Dental Determination of Age. *Journal of the American Dental Association,* 41:45-54.
Hansen, G.
  1953-54. Die Altersbestimmung am proximalen Humerus- und Femurende im Rahmen der Identifizierung menschlicher Skelettreste. *Wissenschaftliche Zeitschrift der Humboldt-Universität zu Berlin,* 3:1-73.
Johnson, L. C.
  1962. Joint Remodeling as the Basis for Osteoarthritis. *Journal of the American Veterinary Medicine Association,* 141:1237- ?
Jowsey, Jenifer.
  1960. Age Changes in Human Bone. *Clinical Orthopaedics,* 17:210-17.
Kerley, Ellis R.
  1965. The Microscopic Determination of Age in Human Bones. *American Journal of Physical Anthropology,* 23:149-63.

_____

  1969. Age Determination of Bone Fragments. *Journal of Forensic Sciences,* 14:59-67.
Krogman, W. M.
  1939. A Guide to the Identification of Human Skeletal Material. *FBI Law Enforcement Bulletin,* 8:3-31.
McKern, Thomas W., and Stewart, T. D.
  1957. Skeletal Age Changes in Young American Males. *Technical Report EP-45.* Quartermaster Research and Development Command, Natick, Mass.
Miles, A. E. W.
  1963. Dentition in the Estimation of Age. *Journal of Dental Research,* 42 (Supplement): 255-63.
Schranz, D.
  1959. Age Determination from Internal Structure of the Humerus. *American Journal of Physical Anthropology,* 17:273-7.
Singer, R.
  1953. Estimation of Age from Cranial Suture Closure. *Journal of Forensic Medicine,* 1:52-9.
Stewart, T. D.
  1954. Evaluation of Evidence from the Skeleton. Chapter 17 in *Legal Medicine* (R. B. H. Gradwohl, editor), C. V. Mosby Co., St. Louis, Mo.

_____

  1958. The Rate of Development of Vertebral Osteoarthritis in American Males and its Significance in Skeletal Identification. *The Leech* (Johannesburg), 28:144-51.

_____

  1961. Sternal Ribs are Aid in Identifying Animal Remains. *FBI Law Enforcement Bulletin,* 30:9-11.
Todd, T. W.
  1920-21. Age Changes in the Pubic Bone. *American Journal of Physical Anthropology,* 3:285-334; 4:1-70, 407-24.
Todd, T. W., and Lyon, D. W., Jr.
  1924-25. Endocranial Suture Closure; Its Progress and Age Relationship. *American Journal of Physical Anthropology,* 7:326-84; 8:23-71, 149-68.

Estimation of Stature from Intact Long Limb Bones

Mildred Trotter

The stature of an individual is an inherent characteristic, the estimate of which is considered to be an important assessment in the identification of an unknown human remains. Such identification is at best putative, it being alleged from evidence which matches, or resembles, the facts known about an individual whose circumstances of death or disappearance are not at variance with those in which the remains are found. But stature is affected by posture, age, and death. So it becomes important, not only to employ the best possible procedure to measure the remains at hand, but also to know the extent to which an estimate, whether derived from direct measurement of the intact dead body, or from the measurement of one or more long limb bones, should be adjusted in order to be accordant with the stature as measured on the living individual.

Most workers who have concerned themselves with the problem of stature estimation, by relating the measurement of cadaver stature to lengths of intact long limb bones, have not been unaware of these difficulties, nor of the need for uniform conditions in order to achieve comparable results. The pioneering report by Rollet (1888) indicated that bones in the "dry state" are, on an average, two millimeters shorter than in the "fresh state." In reevaluating Rollet's data, Manouvrier (1892 and 1893) excluded those subjects 60 years of age and over—50% of Rollet's original number of 100, equally divided between the sexes—because of the effect of "old age," and he also directed that two centimeters be subtracted from the statures that were estimated according to his tables if the statures of the living were desired. Pearson (1899) made a most valuable contribution to the problem by introducing regression equations, which he derived from Rollet's data, and also in recognizing that stature regression equations should not be extended from one "local race" to another without caution because "stature is quite as marked a racial character as cephalic index." The need for this caution was confirmed by Stevenson in 1929 by a comparison of his findings on northern Chinese cadavers with Pearson's analysis of Rollet's data on French cadavers.

Measurements of stature and long limb bones of a large group of young German males were used in regression equations by Breitinger (1937). The clear advantage of stature being measured on the living subject was unfortunately offset by the limited accuracy with which bones can be measured from bony prominences palpated through the skin.

Advantage was taken of the opportunity to collect such highly propitious data; viz., stature measured on the living subject and lengths of the long bones of his free limbs measured on the skeleton, during the United States Repatriation Program following World War II. It is interesting that Rollet's data of 1888 served this program until 1952, either in the form of tables planned differently by Rollet and Manouvrier (average length of a given long bone from those who had the same stature versus average stature of those who presented the same lengths of a given long bone), or in the form of Pearson's regression equations. The purpose of this paper is to summarize the results that developed in our laboratory from this unusual opportunity to assemble data from the same individual before and after death.

Briefly, these results include:

1. A figure to transform stature, measured on the cadaver, to stature measured on the living or vice versa;
2. Some evidence that the average statures of American Whites and Negroes born between 1840 and 1924 are not constant;
3. The amount of loss of adult stature with aging;
4. The regression equations, with standard errors, based on dry, intact long limb bones that can be used to estimate stature in American Whites and Negroes of both sexes, and also in American male citizens described as Mongoloid, Mexican, and Puerto Rican.

Material

The data were drawn from both military and civilian sources. War victims of both World War II and the Korean War, whose identity had never been lost, constitute the military source and are limited to males. Statures of these men had been measured at various centers at the time of induction; the lengths of the long limb bones of World War II victims were measured during the repatriation period by the writer, and the data of the Korean War victims were submitted by Dr. Russell W. Newman of the Quartermaster Research and Engineering Command. The civilian subjects were cadavers of both sexes assigned to Washington University School of Medicine by the Missouri State Anatomical Board; their statures had been measured upon arrival at the medical school; and, their skeletons, as part of the Terry Anatomical Collection (then in our laboratory, now in the Smithsonian Institution), were available for long limb bone measurements.

The number of individuals studied in each of these groups is as follows:

	World War II Males	Korean War Males	Terry Collection Males	Terry Collection Females	Total Studied
White	710	2817	255	63	3845
Negro	80	385	360	177	1002
Mongoloid		68			68
Mexican		63			63
Puerto Rican		49			49
Total studied	790	3382	615	240	5027

The figures do not include 410 World War II and 2135 Korean War personnel, who were under 18 years of age when their stature was measured, or those from whom too few long limb bones were available for measurement, or who were eliminated for both reasons.

Methods

If the results of our studies are to be applied to identification problems, it is essential to describe the methods of taking the measurements, since uniformity of technique is one of the critical factors in work of this kind. It follows, for example, that a more precise stature estimate will be achieved, on the average, if the long bone of the unknown is measured by the same technique that was used for the measurements on which the stature estimation equation was based; or that the figure to transform cadaver stature to living stature will provide a more precise estimate of living stature if the stature of the unknown is measured by the same technique that was used to determine the figure of transformation.

Stature of the military personnel had been measured, as indicated above, at many different stations and by many different workers. It can only be hoped, and assumed, that all were made according to War Department Regulations, 1944, which read, in part as follows:

"10. Directions for taking height. Use a board at least 2 inches wide by 80 inches long, placed vertically, and carefully graduated to ¼ inch between 58 inches from the floor and the top end. Obtain the height by placing vertically, in firm contact with the top of the head, against the measuring rod an accurately square board of about 6 by 6 by 2 inches, best permanently attached to graduated board by a long cord. The individual should stand erect with back to the graduated board, eyes straight to the front. The shoes should be removed when the height is taken."

It was necessary to transform the stature records into centimeters.

The stature measurements of the Terry Collection subjects had been made on a specially constructed vertical measuring panel to which was attached a metric scale and a footboard:

"With careful attention to the several details involved in posing and fixing the cadaver on the panel, the characteristic features of the standing posture can be reproduced: ankles bent, knees and hips extended, lumbar curve produced, shoulders squared and arms hanging at the sides, the face front and eye-ear plane horizontal." (Terry, 1940)

Each subject was photographed on the panel in anterior and lateral views (Figure 20), which thus permitted a correction in the stature measurement when, for example, the heels had not been flat on the foot board.

To measure the maximum length of the 12 long limb bones of the World War II and Terry Collection series (and it is believed to be the technique for the Korean War series), an osteometric board (Figure 21) was used. It had a metric scale,

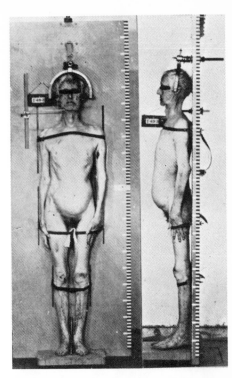

Figure 20. A cadaver posed on the measuring panel (from Terry, 1940).

Figure 21. Osteometric board.

graduated in mm, that extended along the length of the horizontal base from zero, at the fixed vertical part, to 65 cm, together with a squared block of light wood as wide as the board. The procedure was as follows:

Humerus. The head was applied to the vertical part of the osteometric board, the bone was held by the left hand, the block was applied horizonally to the distal extremity, and then the bone was raised slightly and moved up and down, as well as from side to side, until a maximum length was determined (Hrdlička, 1947).

Radius. Same method.

Ulna. Same method.

Femur. The medial condyle was applied to the vertical part of the osteometric board, and then measurement was made in the same way as that for the maximum length of the superior limb bones (Martin, 1928).

Tibia. The end of the malleolus was placed against the vertical wall of the osteometric board, the bone resting on its dorsal surface with its long axis parallel with the long axis of the board. The block was then applied to the most prominent part of the lateral half of lateral condyle.

Fibula. Same method used for superior limb bones (Hrdlička, 1947) is used for the fibula.

In deriving the equations from World War II and Terry Collection data, the lengths of the paired bones were averaged; for the Korean War data, separate equations were derived for right and left bones, and later these were combined for each of the five racial groups. (For the combined equations in the White group, the age was limited to 21 years and older.) If only one bone is available, it is understood that the length of the single bone be used in the equation; the advantage of using the average of the pair is very slight.

The statistical analyses were directed primarily at deriving regression equations that related stature to a given bone length, or for multiple regression equations that related stature to more than one bone length. The method, introduced into this field by Karl Pearson in 1899, is based on a linear relationship between the variables (stature and length of long limb bones) which again was tested and found to be satisfactory. The result of the test is demonstrated in Figure 22. For this figure, the

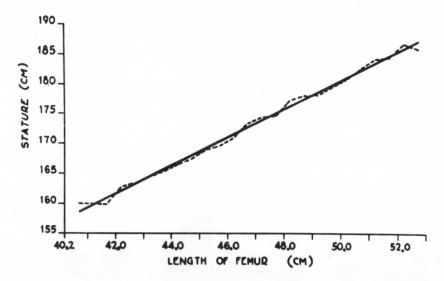

Figure 22. Regression line and mean statures of 710 military White males grouped according to increments of 0.5 cm in the maximum length of the femur (from Trotter and Gleser, 1952, Fig. 1).

mean statures, which correspond to increments of 0.5 cm in the length of the femur, were computed for the 710 White military males (World War II). The resulting averages were plotted and connected by a dotted line; the solid line represents the best fit regression line, which is expressed in the equation:

$$2.38 \text{ Femur length (cm)} + 61.41 \text{ cm} \pm 3.27 \text{ cm}.$$

To estimate the stature of an unknown American White male with an average femoral length of 511 mm, or 51.1 cm, this length, in cm, should be multiplied by the factor 2.38 (121.618 cm) and the result added to 61.41 cm; the stature estimate is thus 183.02 cm, or 72.05 inches (see Table XXVIII and its Appendix 1). The last figure (3.27 cm) in the equation is the standard error for the estimate of stature that is estimated from the length of the femur of any individual who belongs to, or fits in with, this sample. For the example shown, it means that 68% of such estimates may be expected to fall between 179.75 cm and 186.29 cm; that 95% may be expected to fall within the range of two standard errors for the estimate, or between 176.48 cm and 189.56 cm. The remaining 5% of the estimates can be expected to differ very significantly from the true stature.

In addition, the civilian, or Terry Collection, data afforded a determination of the rate of decrease in stature with age through separation of age and secular changes. The combined World War II and civilian data permitted a survey of possible trends in maximum adult stature of American White and Negro males born over a range of 85 years. A comparison of stature estimations for White males of the military and civilian groups, made by applying the stature regression equation derived from one group to the bone lengths of the other, revealed the difference between statures measured on the living and on the cadaver by the Terry method.

Throughout these studies, Dr. Goldine Gleser provided invaluable statistical help.

Loss of Stature with Age

The amount of stature loss (Trotter and Gleser, 1951a) was determined from data that pertained to the Terry Collection subjects. The latter had been received in the laboratory over a period of 22 years, had an age range from 19 to 91 years, and included both Whites and Negroes of both sexes. It was possible to separate the effect of the secular factor (attributed to evolutionary trend, climatic environment, diet, exercise, etc.) on stature from the aging factor by using measurements of stature and long bones (the femur, tibia, and humerus were chosen). Decline in stature with age is independent of the lengths of long bones, which are believed not to change, and which bear high correlations with stature. A series of samples from any given population may differ from each other in average stature; but at the same time the average length of the long bones will also differ in the same direction. Thus, a change in the average stature of successive age groups of a given population will not be accompanied by a corresponding change in the average length of the long bones. From these data, a change in stature with age that is not associated with variance in bone length was obtained by means of partial correlations for the groups of American Whites and Negroes of each sex. These four race-sex groups were found to be alike with respect to the degree of relationship between stature and age, and their weighted average gave an estimate of decrease in stature for this population of 0.06 cm per year, or 1.2 cm in 20 years. Thirty years was assumed to be the age at which stature begins to decrease.

As a check on the universality of this rate of decrease in stature with age, the data presented by Rollet were tested by the same technique. It was found that the average rate of decline, for both the French males and females, was in close agreement with the rate found for American Whites and Negroes. Thus, for individuals over 30 years old, the measured stature may be corrected for age as follows: Stature in cm − 0.06 (age − 30) cm.

Effect of the Secular Factor on Stature

The reason for introducing this subject into this paper is to emphasize the high correlation between long bone length and stature, and to note that, from long bone lengths of archeological or other museum specimens, a good indication of the stature of that population may be gained. Our data suggest that, the older the individual, the less likely he was to have attained a stature as tall as younger individuals living in the same period, but the reverse might be the case for other groups, or even for American Whites and Negroes, living in another era.

The data were drawn from the Terry Collection and from 530 Whites and 81 Negroes of the military series. Stature measurements, the lengths of femora and tibiae, and the year of birth were used. The years of birth extend from 1840 to 1924. The measurement averages were determined according to years of birth, grouped in decennia for the civilian subjects, and in quinquennia for the military personnel. The stature measurements of the civilian subjects were adjusted in order to be comparable with those of the military subjects. In order to reveal the trends in stature, running averages, based on figures of three successive time periods, were determined both for stature and for the sum of the lengths of femur and tibia. (By this means, sampling fluctuations and the possible effects of statistically small samples tend to be annulled.) There was found to be a relatively constant average stature and average length of femur plus tibia devoid of any trend, for all four groups born between 1840 and 1895; but for the two groups (only White and Negro males were available) born between 1905 and 1924 there was a significant increase in both stature and long bone lengths (Trotter and Gleser, 1951b).

Gain in Stature with Death

It is of interest to recall that Rollet, Manouvrier, and Pearson differed in their recommendations of a figure to transform stature measured on the cadaver to stature measured on the living, even though they were concerned with the same data. It is possible that no one value can be applied in general since it is quite likely that the amount of adjustment needed will differ according to the method used in measuring stature, especially the stature of the cadaver. Those attempting to compare the average stature from a sample of cadavers with the average stature from a sample of the living population should make sure that both samples are truly random, that they lived during the same period, and that neither was undergoing a secular trend.

For the present samples, the average difference between cadaver (civilian) and living (military) statures was determined on the basis of equations for the estimation of stature for White males that came from the two sources. This method is feasible since secular trends in stature had been shown to be accompanied by corresponding trends in the length of long bones. The difference between the estimated cadaver stature of the White military males and their living stature was 2.69 cm. On the other hand, the difference between the estimated living stature of the White Terry Collection males and their cadaver stature (adjusted for age) was 2.35 cm. Thus, the average cadaver stature was considered to be 2.5 cm greater than the living stature and vice versa. It is reasonable to assume that the gain in stature with death is constant for a particular method of measurement (Trotter and Gleser, 1952).

Regression Equations for the Estimation of Stature

The best fitting linear equation for the estimation of stature of young adult Americans, including the standard error of estimate, from the length of each long limb bone, was obtained from the data for each sample studied; i.e., both after World War II and the Korean War. This resulted in equations for: White and Negro males from World War II, the Korean War, and from Terry Collection data; for White and Negro females from Terry Collection data; and for Mongoloid, Mexican, and Puerto Rican males from Korean War data. Multiple regression equations were also derived for the estimation of stature from the lengths of two or more long limb bones in various combinations and these were compared with the equations derived from one bone (see Trotter and Gleser, 1952 and 1958).

Among the facts presented by these equations, it may be noted that: an estimate of stature had a smaller standard error when computed from bones of the inferior limb than from bones of the superior limb; the standard error of estimate was smaller for all equations based on military personnel data than for comparable equations based on the Terry Collection, which indicates again that stature measured on the living individual introduces less error variance than when measured on the dead; and, that comparable equations for White and Negro males, which were derived from the two sets of military data, show very slight differences of no statistical significance, and with slightly smaller standard errors of estimate for the first series than for the second.

For these, and other, more or less arbitrary reasons the equations for the estimation of living, adult, maximum stature of American Whites and Negroes of both sexes, and of American Mongoloid and Mexican males presented in Table XXVIII were selected as the most likely at the present time to give satisfactory estimates for unknowns belonging to these groups. The equations that are applicable to White and Negro males are from World War II data, those for the females are from the Terry Collection data as corrected for age and stature as measured on the cadaver, and those for Mongoloid and Mexican males are from the Korean War data. It is safe to say that the equations for the Whites and Negroes have been based on random samples and, thus, give reliable estimates. For the convenience of those who wish to use these equations, stature estimates were derived by applying them to successive lengths of the long limb bones and the results are presented as Appendixes 1 to 4 of Table XXVIII.

TABLE XXVIII
Equations to Estimate Living Stature (cm)—with Standard Errors—from the Long Bones of American Whites and Negroes Between 18 and 30 Years of Age*

White Males		Negro Males	
3.08 Hum + 70.45	± 4.05	3.26 Hum + 62.10	± 4.43
3.78 Rad + 79.01	± 4.32	3.42 Rad + 81.56	± 4.30
3.70 Ulna + 74.05	± 4.32	3.26 Ulna + 79.29	± 4.42
2.38 Fem + 61.41	± 3.27	2.11 Fem + 70.35	± 3.94
2.52 Tib + 78.62	± 3.37	2.19 Tib + 86.02	± 3.78
2.68 Fib + 71.78	± 3.29	2.19 Fib + 85.65	± 4.08
1.30 (Fem + Tib) + 63.29	± 2.99	1.15 (Fem + Tib) + 71.04	± 3.53

White Females		Negro Females	
3.36 Hum + 57.97	± 4.45	3.08 Hum + 64.67	± 4.25
4.74 Rad + 54.93	± 4.24	2.75 Rad + 94.51	± 5.05
4.27 Ulna + 57.76	± 4.30	3.31 Ulna + 75.38	± 4.83
2.47 Fem + 54.10	± 3.72	2.28 Fem + 59.76	± 3.41
2.90 Tib + 61.53	± 3.66	2.45 Tib + 72.65	± 3.70
2.93 Fib + 59.61	± 3.57	2.49 Fib + 70.90	± 3.80
1.39 (Fem + Tib) + 53.20	± 3.55	1.26 (Fem + Tib) + 59.72	± 3.28

Mongoloid Males		Mexican Males	
2.68 Hum + 83.19	± 4.25	2.92 Hum + 73.94·	± 4.24
3.54 Rad + 82.00	± 4.60	3.55 Rad + 80.71	± 4.04
3.48 Ulna + 77.45	± 4.66	3.56 Ulna + 74.56	± 4.05
2.15 Fem + 72.57	± 3.80	2.44 Fem + 58.67	± 2.99
2.39 Tib + 81.45	± 3.27	2.36 Tib + 80.62	± 3.73
2.40 Fib + 80.56	± 3.24	2.50 Fib + 75.44	± 3.52
1.22 (Fem + Tib) + 70.37	± 3.24		

*To estimate stature of older individuals subtract 0.06 (age in years — 30) cm; to estimate cadaver stature, add 2.5 cm.

TABLE XXVIII

APPENDIX 1—Expected maximum stature* from long bone lengths (maximum) for American White males

Hum	Rad	Ulna	Stature		Fem	Tib	Fib	Fem + Tib
mm	mm	mm	cm	in**	mm	mm	mm	mm
265	193	211	152	59^7	381	291	299	685
268	196	213	153	60^2	385	295	303	693
271	198	216	154	60^5	389	299	307	701
275	201	219	155	61	393	303	311	708
278	204	222	156	61^3	398	307	314	716
281	206	224	157	61^6	402	311	318	723
284	209	227	158	62^2	406	315	322	731
288	212	230	159	62^5	410	319	326	738
291	214	232	160	63	414	323	329	746
294	217	235	161	63^3	419	327	333	753
297	220	238	162	63^6	423	331	337	761
301	222	240	163	64^1	427	335	340	769
304	225	243	164	64^5	431	339	344	776
307	228	246	165	65	435	343	348	784
310	230	249	166	65^3	440	347	352	791
314	233	251	167	65^6	444	351	355	799
317	235	254	168	66^1	448	355	359	806
320	238	257	169	66^4	452	359	363	814
323	241	259	170	66^7	456	363	367	821
327	243	262	171	67^3	461	367	370	829
330	246	265	172	67^6	465	371	374	837
333	249	267	173	68^1	469	375	378	844
336	251	270	174	68^4	473	379	381	852
339	254	273	175	68^7	477	383	385	859
343	257	276	176	69^2	482	386	389	867
346	259	278	177	69^5	486	390	393	874
349	262	281	178	70^1	490	394	396	882
352	265	284	179	70^4	494	398	400	889
356	267	286	180	70^7	498	402	404	897
359	270	289	181	71^2	503	406	408	905
362	272	292	182	71^5	507	410	411	912
365	275	294	183	72	511	414	415	920
369	278	297	184	72^4	515	418	419	927
372	280	300	185	72^7	519	422	422	935
375	283	303	186	73^2	524	426	426	942
378	286	305	187	73^5	528	430	430	950
382	288	308	188	74	532	434	434	957
385	291	311	189	74^3	536	438	437	965
388	294	313	190	74^6	540	442	441	973
391	296	316	191	75^2	545	446	445	980
395	299	319	192	75^5	549	450	449	988
398	302	321	193	76	553	454	452	995
401	304	324	194	76^3	557	458	456	1003
404	307	327	195	76^6	561	462	460	1010
408	309	330	196	77^1	566	466	463	1018
411	312	332	197	77^4	570	470	467	1026
414	315	335	198	78	574	474	471	1033

*The expected maximum stature should be reduced by the amount of 0.06 (age in years — 30) cm to obtain expected stature of individuals over 30 years of age.

**The raised number indicates the numerator of a fraction of an inch expressed in eighths, thus 59^7 should be read 59⅞ inches.

TABLE XXVIII

APPENDIX 2—Expected maximum stature* from long bone lengths (maximum) for American Negro males

Hum	Rad	Ulna	Stature		Fem	Tib	Fib	Fem + Tib
mm	mm	mm	cm	in**	mm	mm	mm	mm
276	206	223	152	59^7	387	301	303	704
279	209	226	153	60^2	391	306	308	713
282	212	229	154	60^5	396	310	312	721
285	215	232	155	61	401	315	317	730
288	218	235	156	61^3	406	320	321	739
291	221	238	157	61^6	410	324	326	747
294	224	242	158	62^2	415	329	330	756
297	226	245	159	62^5	420	333	335	765
300	229	248	160	63	425	338	339	774
303	232	251	161	63^3	430	342	344	782
306	235	254	162	63^6	434	347	349	791
310	238	257	163	64^1	439	352	353	800
313	241	260	164	64^5	444	356	358	808
316	244	263	165	65	449	361	362	817
319	247	266	166	65^3	453	365	367	826
322	250	269	167	65^6	458	370	371	834
325	253	272	168	66^1	463	374	376	843
328	256	275	169	66^4	468	379	381	852
331	259	278	170	66^7	472	383	385	861
334	262	281	171	67^3	477	388	390	869
337	264	284	172	67^6	482	393	394	878
340	267	287	173	68^1	487	397	399	887
343	270	291	174	68^4	491	402	403	895
346	273	294	175	68^7	496	406	408	904
349	276	297	176	69^2	501	411	413	913
352	279	300	177	69^5	506	415	417	921
356	282	303	178	70	510	420	422	930
359	285	306	179	70^1	515	425	426	939
362	288	309	180	70^7	520	429	431	947
365	291	312	181	71^2	525	434	435	956
368	294	315	182	71^5	529	438	440	965
371	297	318	183	72	534	443	445	974
374	300	321	184	72^4	539	447	449	982
377	302	324	185	72^7	544	452	454	991
380	305	327	186	73^2	548	456	458	1000
383	308	330	187	73^5	553	461	463	1008
386	311	333	188	74	558	466	467	1017
389	314	336	189	74^3	563	470	472	1026
392	317	340	190	74^6	567	475	476	1034
395	320	343	191	75^2	572	479	481	1043
398	323	346	192	75^5	577	484	486	1052
401	326	349	193	76	582	488	490	1061
405	329	352	194	76^3	586	493	495	1069
408	332	355	195	76^6	591	498	499	1078
411	335	358	196	77^1	596	502	504	1087
414	337	361	197	77^4	601	507	508	1095
417	340	364	198	78	605	511	513	1104

*The expected maximum stature should be reduced by the amount of 0.06 (age in years — 30) cm to obtain expected stature of individuals over 30 years of age.

**The raised number indicates the numerator of a fraction of an inch expressed in eighths, thus 59^7 should be read 59⅞ inches.

TABLE XXVIII

APPENDIX 3—Expected maximum stature* from long bone lengths (maximum) for American White females

Hum	Rad	Ulna	Stature		Fem	Tib	Fib	Fem + Tib
mm	mm	mm	cm	in**	mm	mm	mm	mm
244	179	193	140	55^1	348	271	274	624
247	182	195	141	55^4	352	274	278	632
250	184	197	142	55^7	356	277	281	639
253	186	200	143	56^2	360	281	285	646
256	188	202	144	56^6	364	284	288	653
259	190	204	145	57^1	368	288	291	660
262	192	207	146	57^4	372	291	295	668
265	194	209	147	57^7	376	295	298	675
268	196	211	148	58^2	380	298	302	682
271	198	214	149	58^5	384	302	305	689
274	201	216	150	59	388	305	309	696
277	203	218	151	59^4	392	309	312	704
280	205	221	152	59^7	396	312	315	711
283	207	223	153	60^2	400	315	319	718
286	209	225	154	60^5	404	319	322	725
289	211	228	155	61	409	322	326	732
292	213	230	156	61^3	413	326	329	740
295	215	232	157	61^6	417	329	332	747
298	217	235	158	62^2	421	333	336	754
301	220	237	159	62^5	425	336	340	761
304	222	239	160	63	429	340	343	768
307	224	242	161	63^3	433	343	346	776
310	226	244	162	63^6	437	346	349	783
313	228	246	163	64^1	441	350	353	790
316	230	249	164	64^5	445	353	356	797
319	232	251	165	65	449	357	360	804
322	234	253	166	65^3	453	360	363	812
324	236	256	167	65^6	457	364	366	819
327	239	258	168	66^1	461	367	370	826
330	241	261	169	66^4	465	371	373	833
333	243	263	170	66^7	469	374	377	840
336	245	265	171	67^3	473	377	380	847
339	247	268	172	67^6	477	381	384	855
342	249	270	173	68^1	481	384	387	862
345	251	272	174	68^4	485	388	390	869
348	253	275	175	68^7	489	391	394	876
351	255	277	176	69^2	494	395	397	883
354	258	279	177	69^5	498	398	401	891
357	260	282	178	70^1	502	402	404	898
360	262	284	179	70^4	506	405	407	905
363	264	286	180	70^7	510	409	411	912
366	266	289	181	71^2	514	412	414	919
369	268	291	182	71^5	518	415	418	927
372	270	293	183	72	522	419	421	934
375	272	296	184	72^4	526	422	425	941

*The expected maximum stature should be reduced by the amount of 0.06 (age in years — 30) cm to obtain expected stature of individuals over 30 years of age.

**The raised number indicates the numerator of a fraction of an inch expressed in eighths, thus 55^1 should be read 55⅛ inches.

TABLE XXVIII

APPENDIX 4—Expected maximum stature* from long bone lengths (maximum) for American Negro females

Hum	Rad	Ulna	Stature		Fem	Tib	Fib	Fem + Tib
mm	mm	mm	cm	in**	mm	mm	mm	mm
245	165	195	140	55^1	352	275	278	637
248	169	198	141	55^4	356	279	282	645
251	173	201	142	55^7	361	283	286	653
254	176	204	143	56^2	365	287	290	661
258	180	207	144	56^6	369	291	294	669
261	184	210	145	57^1	374	295	298	677
264	187	213	146	57^4	378	299	302	685
267	191	216	147	57^7	383	303	306	693
271	195	219	148	58^2	387	308	310	701
274	198	222	149	58^5	391	312	314	709
277	202	225	150	59	396	316	318	717
280	205	228	151	59^4	400	320	322	724
284	209	231	152	59^7	405	324	326	732
287	213	235	153	60^2	409	328	330	740
290	216	238	154	60^5	413	332	334	748
293	220	241	155	61	418	336	338	756
297	224	244	156	61^3	422	340	342	764
300	227	247	157	61^6	426	344	346	772
303	231	250	158	62^2	431	348	350	780
306	235	253	159	62^5	435	352	354	788
310	238	256	160	63	440	357	358	796
313	242	259	161	63^3	444	361	362	804
316	245	262	162	63^6	448	365	366	812
319	249	265	163	64^1	453	369	370	820
322	253	268	164	64^5	457	373	374	828
326	256	271	165	65	462	377	378	836
329	260	274	166	65^3	466	381	382	843
332	264	277	167	65^6	470	385	386	851
335	267	280	168	66^1	475	389	390	859
339	271	283	169	66^4	479	393	394	867
342	275	286	170	66^7	484	397	398	875
345	278	289	171	67^3	488	401	402	883
348	282	292	172	67^6	492	406	406	891
352	285	295	173	68^1	497	410	410	899
355	289	298	174	68^4	501	414	414	907
358	293	301	175	68^7	505	418	418	915
361	296	304	176	69^2	510	422	422	923
365	300	307	177	69^5	514	426	426	931
368	304	310	178	70^1	519	430	430	939
371	307	313	179	70^4	523	434	434	947
374	311	316	180	70^7	527	438	438	955
378	315	319	181	71^2	532	442	442	963
381	318	322	182	71^5	536	446	446	970
384	322	325	183	72	541	450	450	978
387	325	328	184	72^4	545	454	454	986

*The expected maximum stature should be reduced by the amount of 0.06 (age in years — 30) cm to obtain expected stature of individuals over 30 years of age.

**The raised number indicates the numerator of a fraction of an inch expressed in eighths, thus 55^1 should be read 55⅛ inches.

The equations derived from the American Puerto Rican data are practically identical with those of the Negro males for every bone except the humerus, which indicates the similarity between the proportions of the length of limb to stature for the two groups, and even though the average stature of the Puerto Rican was approximately 7.0 cm shorter than that of the Negro. It is suggested that the Negro male equations be applied to Puerto Rican males until a modification is indicated by a study of a larger and more representative sample. It is not known whether the same bodily proportions obtain for the females of these two American groups.

The equations derived from the American Mongoloid and Mexican data are also subject to a considerable sampling error because of the relatively small numbers; in addition, the Mongoloid series was admittedly heterogeneous; it included Japanese, Hawaiians, Filipinos, American Indians, etc. The equations from the two groups are similar, and both resulted in stature estimates that were too tall for Mexicans of World War II, but for these groups the Mexican equations provided more reliable estimates than did the Mongoloid equations, which thus indicate that the ratio of long limb bones to stature differ in the two groups. Genovés' study in 1967 on the relation of long bones to stature was limited to a very small homogeneous sample of "indigenous" Mesoamericans, whose average statures were 162 cm for males, and 150 cm for females. Since the average stature of the American group of Mexican males was 168.65 cm, it is not likely that Genovés' sample represents the immigrants from Mexico to the United States. Rather, he succeeded in his aim to provide formulae for stature estimation for the descendants of the prehispanic population of Mesoamerica. It is probable that the immigrants from Mexico to the United States are descendants of later settlers, but with a more or less admixture of the earlier population. Thus, looking toward better stature estimation equations, the need continues for a random-sample study of both Mexicans and American Indians.

There is abundant evidence to indicate that, in general, the most accurate estimates of stature are obtained when the equation applied to the unknown has been derived from a representative sample of the population of the same sex, race, age, geographical area, and time period to which the unknown is believed to belong. This may be illustrated by comparing our method of stature estimation with the methods of five different investigators (Manouvrier's table, 1892, based on Rollet's French cadavers of the last century; Pearson's equation, 1899, based on the same series of French data; Breitinger's equation, 1937, based on measurements of living Germans; Telkkä's equation, 1950, derived from measurements of Finnish skeletons of the same time period as our own equation; and, Dupertuis and Hadden's equation, 1951, again of the same time period as our own, but based on uncorrected cadaver stature), using as a test the estimation of stature from the length of the femur, when applied to 100 American White military males (not part of the group on which our equation was based). Our equation, which was derived from essentially the same population, however, resulted in a mean error of estimate of only −0.02 cm, whereas the mean errors of the others were either too low (ranging from −1.66 cm to −4.38 cm) or too high (+3.22 cm). Another example of the need to apply the appropriate equation is seen in the work of Allbrook (1961), who found that a different regression equation was necessary to estimate stature from bone lengths for each of five different tribal groups in East Africa.

In conclusion, a few reminders are in order:
- Any one of the equations resulting from our studies should be applied only to dry bones without cartilage.
- Never use a superior limb bone to estimate stature when an inferior limb bone is available. Inferior limb bone lengths are more highly correlated with stature than are superior limb bone lengths and, therefore, they may be expected to provide a more reliable estimate of stature.
- Be ever mindful of the fact that an estimation of stature is a statistical problem that depends for its reliability upon the random quality of the sample

from which the equation was derived, upon accuracy of the bone measurement made according to the same techniques as were those for the equation, and upon an agreement of race, sex, age, and time period between the unknown and the sample providing the equation.

● And, finally, always remember that a stature estimate is only one piece of evidence among the many that provide a putative identification.

Literature Cited

Allbrook, David
1961. The Estimation of Stature in British and East African Males. *Journal of Forensic Medicine,* 8:15-28.

Breitinger, E.
1937. Zur Berechnung der Körperhöhe aus den langen Gliedmassenknochen. *Anthropologischer Anzeiger,* 14:249-274.

Dupertuis, C. W., and Hadden, J. A., Jr.
1951. On the Reconstruction of Stature from Long Bones. *American Journal of Physical Anthropology,* new series, 9:15-54.

Hrdlička, A.
1947. *Practical Anthropometry.* 3d edition, edited by T. D. Stewart. Wistar Institute, Philadelphia. 230 pages.

Genovés, S.
1967. Proportionality of the Long Bones and Their Relation to Stature Among Mesoamericans. *American Journal of Physical Anthropology,* 26:67-78.

Manouvrier, L.
1892. Determination de la taille d'après les grands os des membres. *Revue Mensuelle de l'Ecole d'Anthropologie,* 2:227-233.

———
1893. Le determination de la taille d'après les grands os des membres. *Mémoirs de la Société d'Anthropologie de Paris.* 2d series, 4:347-402.

Martin, R.
1928. *Lehrbuch der Anthropologie.* 2d edition. 3 volumes. Gustav Fischer, Jena.

Pearson, K.
1899. IV. Mathematical Contributions to the Theory of Evolution. V. On the Reconstruction of the Stature of Prehistoric Races. *Philosophical Transactions of the Royal Society.* Series A, 192:169-244.

Rollet, E.
1888. *De la mensuration des os longs des membres.* Thèse pour le doctorat en médecine, 1st series, 43:1-128.

Stevenson, P. H.
1929. On Racial Differences in Stature Long Bone Regression Formulae, with Special Reference to Stature Reconstruction Formulae for the Chinese. *Biometrika,* 21:303-321.

Telkkä, A.
1950. On the Prediction of Human Stature from the Long Bones. *Acta Anatomica,* 9:103-117.

Terry, R. J.
1940. On Measuring and Photographing the Cadaver. *American Journal of Physical Anthropology,* 26:433-447.

Trotter, Mildred, and Gleser, Goldine C.
1951a. The Effect of Ageing on Stature. *American Journal of Physical Anthropology,* 9:311-324.

———
1951b. Trends in Stature of American Whites and Negroes Born Between 1840 and 1924. *American Journal of Physical Anthropology,* 9:427-440.

———
1952. Estimation of Stature from Long Bones of American Whites and Negroes. *American Journal of Physical Anthropology,* 10:463-514.

———
1958. A Re-evaluation of Estimation of Stature Based on Measurements of Stature Taken During Life and of Long Bones after Death. *American Journal of Physical Anthropology,* 16:79-123.

War Department
1944. *Mobilization Regulations,* section III, paragraphs 9-14.

Estimation of Stature from Fragments of Long Limb Bones*

D. Gentry Steele

Stature is a descriptive characteristic of an individual which, after his death in forensic situations, can contribute importantly to his identification. But from this standpoint, whether stature is as important as other descriptive characteristics, such as age and race, is debatable. Be this as it may, stature becomes obscured, just as do most other descriptive characteristics, when a dead body reaches the skeletonized state, and especially when the individual bones lose their anatomical relationships. In such cases stature can be estimated, as Dr. Trotter has shown in the preceding chapter, if at least one whole long limb bone exists, since there is a relatively high correlation between the length of any whole long limb bone and stature. But what if only fragments of long bones have survived? This, of course, is the situation which confronts those in charge of identification in plane crashes and other types of mass disasters. It can be said here that the potential of limb bone fragments to yield information useful in personal identification should not be overlooked.

Gertrude Müller (1935) is credited with the first attempt to provide a scientific basis for estimates of whole bone lengths from bone fragments—the necessary first step in reconstructing stature. Her approach was to relate definable fragments to the whole bone, for which purpose she used 100 humeri, 50 radii, and 100 tibiae from the Osterreiches Beinhaus in Zellerndorf. For the humerus, she described six landmarks from which she derived five segments and then calculated the percentage of total bone length represented by each. Similarly, for the radius and tibia she described, respectively, five and eight landmarks and four and seven segments, and made the same percentage calculation for each. Müller's percentages enable one to estimate, from a fragment of any one of these three bones, the approximate total length, provided the fragment includes one of the described segments. The resulting figure can then be converted into stature by entering it in an appropriate stature regression formula based upon the same whole bone.

I first realized the value of this technique to estimate total lengths of incomplete bones while working with Dr. Thomas W. McKern on prehistoric Indian skeletons from sites in northeastern Arkansas (Steele and McKern, 1969). But instead of restricting the analysis to simple percentages, we also used the least-squares method of factor analysis to calculate regression formulae for each segment, and for certain combinations of segments, of the femur, tibia, and humerus of both sexes. In departing still further from Müller's example, by using the femur instead of the radius, we recognized that the femur, besides being more closely related to stature than the radius, is also more likely to be represented in prehistoric remains. Thus, our work not only altered Müller's original design as regards the bones used, but it extended

* This work was made possible through the support of a Smithsonian Institution summer research grant and a University of Kansas research grant (#3491-5038). The use of the computer facilities at the University of Kansas was made possible through a computation center grant (#58568). The author would like to extend his thanks to Mr. Gary McClelland for his assistance with statistical data.

its application to a different population and provided, for this new population, a more precise means of estimation through more refined statistical procedures.

Considering Dr. McKern's interest in skeletal identification for forensic purposes, the natural next step was to extend our modification of the Müller technique to the present American population, particularly American Whites and Negroes. In this connection, many investigators (most recently Trotter and Gleser, 1952, 1958; Genovés, 1967) have shown that the formulae used to estimate stature from whole long limb bones must be specific for each racial group. This being the case, there is reason to believe that it is just as important to have equally specific formulae to estimate total bone length from the constituent segments. To this end, I spent part of the summer of 1968 in Washington measuring the White and Negro skeletons of the Terry Collection in the Smithsonian's National Museum of Natural History.

The purpose of the present paper is to report the results of this latest work in a form that can be applied readily in forensic cases.

Material and Methods

The record for each skeleton in the Terry Collection usually includes the individual's name, morgue report, age, race (White or Negro), sex, cadaver weight, and cadaver stature. Also, a photograph of the cadaver in a vertical position on a special measuring board (Terry, 1940; see also Figure 20 in this volume) is included in the majority of records.

The author personally selected approximately 50 skeletons from each of the following race-sex combinations: White male, White female, Negro male, and Negro female. The sample totaled 207. Two criteria had to be satisfied before a skeleton was included in the sample:

1. Its record had to be complete as to age, race, sex, and stature, including a photograph of the cadaver taken at the time stature was measured
2. It had to be free of broken bones and/or extensive arthritic growths around the articular surfaces.

The photograph made possible the confirmation of the race and sex of the individual; it also showed the position of the cadaver at the time of stature measurement. If the feet were not in a natural plantar position on the base of the measuring board, the specimen was rejected. At first, individuals of all ages were included in the sample, but eventually all over 70 years of age were excluded.

Three long bones from the left side—femur, tibia, and humerus—were used in the present study. For measuring purposes, each long bone was placed on a standard osteometric board in the manner recommended by Trotter and Gleser (1952, pages 472-3), except that, in the case of the femur and humerus, the posterior surface faced upwards. Moreover, the position of each bone, for the measurement of maximum length, was maintained during the measurement of its several segments. For the femur, this position was determined by the most superior point on the head and the most inferior point on the medial condyle; for the tibia, it was the most prominent part of the lateral half of the lateral condyle and the end of the malleolus; and for the humerus it was simply the long axis of the diaphysis. It is important to remember this positioning of the bones when the method is being applied to true fragments.

The landmarks and segments of the three long bones that were used in this study had already been selected and defined during the previous work. For the tibia and humerus, they follow rather closely, but are fewer in number, than those defined by Müller. They are limited, however, as a rule, to those that yield the best regressions with maximum length. One landmark, which neither Müller nor I used in defining a segment, is the nutrient foramen. Tests proved to me that the position of this foramen varies widely—relative to all other landmarks used. Also, not infrequently, there are two or more foramena.

Another landmark not used in the present study, but used previously by the author and Dr. McKern, involves the humerus alone. The landmark in question is the point of greatest narrowing at the middle of the diaphysis. Although this narrowing can be related to a point, postero-laterally in the radial groove where the lateral supracondylar ridge becomes indistinct (on a level with the distal termination of the surface for *m. deltoideus*), in practice the point proved impossible to locate with sufficient constancy to give useful results.

The landmarks for the three bones used in the present study are shown in Figure 23 and are defined as follows:

Femur:

1. The most proximal point on the head.
2. The midpoint of the lesser trochanter.

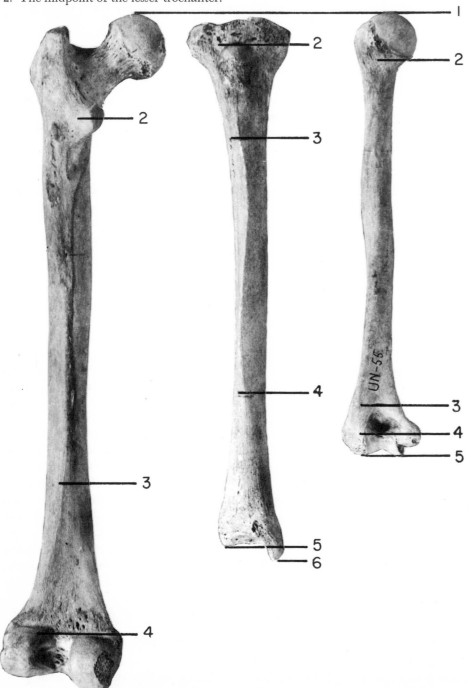

Figure 23. Left femur (posterior aspect), right tibia (anterior aspect), and left humerus (posterior aspect) shown in the positions used to measure their maximum lengths and the lengths of certain defined segments. The numbers refer to landmarks (see page 87 for definitions) and at the same time indicate segments (segment 1 is between landmarks 1 and 2; segment 2 is between landmarks 2 and 3, etc.). Note that the line leading from number 1 does not touch the proximal end of the tibia. This is deliberate and is due to the fact that the landmark here is on the lateral side of the lateral condyle.

3. The most proximal extension of the popliteal surface at the point where the medial and lateral supracondylar lines become parallel below the linea aspera.
4. The most proximal point of the intercondylar fossa.
5. The most distal point of the medial condyle.

Tibia:

1. The most prominent point on the lateral half of the lateral condyle.
2. The most proximal point of the tibial tuberosity.
3. The point of confluence for the lines extending from the lower end of the tuberosity.
4. The point where the anterior crest crosses over to the medial border of the shaft above the medial malleolus.
5. The proximal margin of the inferior articular surface at a point opposite the tip of the medial malleolus.
6. The most distal point on the medial malleolus.

Humerus:

1. The most proximal point on the head.
2. The most distal point of the circumference of the head.
3. The proximal margin of the olecranon fossa.
4. The distal margin of the olecranon fossa.
5. The most distal point on the trochlea.

The numbering of the landmarks from the proximal end of each bone downwards facilitates the comprehension of the system of numbering the segments: Each segment bears the number of the landmark at its proximal end. Thus, segment one is the part of the bone between landmarks one and two; segment two is that between landmarks two and three, etc.

Age, Stature, and Maximum Bone Lengths (Table XXIX)

The average age for each subgroup of the present sample is lower than that of the corresponding subgroups of the larger sample of the Terry Collection reported by Trotter and Gleser (1952). This difference in average age is greatest in the case of the White males, and least in the case of the White females. On the other hand, stature, maximum length of femur, and maximum length of tibia are generally greater in the author's subgroups than in those of Trotter's and Gleser's larger sample. Moreover, so far as the males are concerned, the figures for the author's subgroups tend to be intermediate between those of Trotter and Gleser for both the Terry Collection and the war casualties. This is probably due to the elimination of the older specimens from the present sample. Trotter and Gleser (1951) showed that a slight trend toward increased stature occurred between 1840 and 1909, and that the statistically significant decline of stature with age during that period was not associated with changes in long bone length. Because of these findings, the selection that eliminated the older individuals of the Terry Collection constitutes a selection that eliminated some of the shorter individuals in the Collection. So far as the purpose of the present study is concerned, the difference in average long bone length between the two samples from the Terry Collection is not necessarily detrimental, since the present sample is apparently closer in average size to the modern population than is the total Terry Collection.

Lengths of Long Limb Bone Segments (Tables XXX-XXXII)

The data in the next three tables constitute the basic new data obtained during this study to estimate stature from long limb bone fragments. No attempt has been made to statistically test the significance of the differences shown.

TABLE XXIX
Comparison of the Means (± One Standard Deviation) of Age, Stature, and Three Long Limb Bone Lengths in Different Race-Sex Samples.

Subsample	Number	Age	Stature [1] (cm)	Maximum length (in cm)		
				Femur	Tibia	Humerus
White males						
Terry Collection:						
Trotter & Gleser (1952)	255	61.66±12.25	167.89±7.34	45.66±2.45	36.37±2.17	33.00±1.79
Present study	61	52.97± 4.98	168.44±8.11	46.24±3.06	37.08±2.56	32.85±2.02
War casualties:						
Trotter & Gleser (1952)	545	23.14± 4.31	173.90±6.63	47.29±2.36	37.85±2.19	33.60±1.67
Trotter & Gleser (1958)	1265	—	—	174.39±6.55	47.17±2.30	38.42±2.17	33.53±1.64
Negro males						
Terry Collection:						
Trotter & Gleser (1952)	360	49.46±15.51	170.23±7.81	47.42±2.97	38.72±2.53	33.78±1.88
Present study	42	43.25±13.21	172.02±7.84	47.92±3.28	40.10±2.95	34.23±1.75
War casualties:						
Trotter & Gleser (1952)	54	25.07± 4.98	172.11±6.14	48.34±2.26	39.55±2.30	33.79±1.34
Trotter & Gleser (1958)	191	—	—	173.86±6.65	48.41±2.48	40.32±2.31	34.06±1.67
White females						
Terry Collection:						
Trotter & Gleser (1952)	63	63.93±16.07	158.18±7.51	42.96±2.53	34.03±2.15	30.43±1.73
Present study	52	63.35±17.02	157.62±7.96	42.69±2.71	34.30±2.19	30.18±1.71
Negro females						
Terry Collection:						
Trotter & Gleser (1952)	177	47.21±17.65	158.39±6.53	43.71±2.39	35.42±2.14	30.76±1.58
Present study	57	39.58±15.52	159.88±6.22	43.96±2.30	36.22±2.07	30.68±1.55

[1] Stature for the Terry Collection is cadaver length less 2.5 cm; for the war casualties it is the figure obtained during life.

Correlations (Tables XXXIII-XXXV)

Correlations were developed:

1. Between each long limb bone segment and the maximum length of the bone of which it is a constituent
2. Between each long limb bone segment and stature (= cadaver length less 2.5 cm).

The same process was repeated for various combinations of the segments. The only correlations between combinations of segments and stature included in Tables XXXIII-XXXV, however, are the ones which will provide estimates of total bone length with a standard error below 1.0 cm.

It will be noted that, in the majority of cases, the length of a segment correlates more closely with maximum bone length than with stature. In general, the longer the segment, or the combination of segments, the better the correlation both with maximum bone length and with stature.

Regressions of Segment(s) Length to Maximum Bone Length (Tables XXXVI-XLVII)

The equations, or formulae, that represent the regression of segment(s) length with maximum bone length provide the means to calculate maximum bone length from a fragment that contains one or more of the defined segments. All one needs to do, provided the race is White or Negro and the sex is known, is to substitute in the appropriate formula (as given in the tables) the length of the indicated segment(s), and then to carry out the indicated calculation. For example, if a fragment of a femur from a Negro male is found to include segments two and three, which measure 28.34 and 7.51 cm, respectively, the length of the whole femur can be calculated by reference to the proper formula in Table XXXVII. Thus:

$$1.12(28.34) + 1.13(7.51) + 7.92 = 48.15 \pm 0.67 \text{ cm.}$$

If at this point one wished to estimate the stature corresponding to this femur length, the means are provided by the stature regression formulae of Trotter and Gleser (1952, 1958; see preceding chapter). Using their 1958 formula for the male Negro femur, the first step is as follows:

$$2.10(48.15) + 72.22 = 173.34 \pm 3.91 \text{ cm.}$$

The second step is to adjust the standard error to take into account the fact that the femur length also has a standard error; namely, ± 0.67 cm. Adjustment is made by multiplying the standard error of the estimated femur length by the first constant in the stature regression formula, and then adding the product to the standard error of the estimated stature. Thus:

$$2.10(0.67) + 3.91 = \pm 5.32 \text{ cm.}$$

The estimated stature in this case is therefore 173.34 ± 5.32 cm.

Regressions of the Length of Two or More Segments to Stature (Tables XLVIII-L)

In order to find regression formulae for the present data that yield the best estimates of stature from incomplete long limb bones, the high correlations between multiple segments and stature, mentioned in connection with Tables XXXIII-XXXV, were followed up. The resulting formulae, although yielding lower standard errors than those of Trotter and Gleser, of course, are useful only when the incomplete bones under study lack no more than one or both extremities. Since the example previously used fits into this category, it can be used to show how one of these formulae is applied. The appropriate formulae, from Table XLVIII, is:

$$2.59(\text{Fem. 2}) + 2.91(\text{Fem. 3}) + 75.74 = \text{Stature} \pm 3.72 \text{ cm.}$$

Substituting and calculating:

$$2.59(28.34) + 2.91(7.51) + 75.74 = 170.99 \pm 3.72 \text{ cm.}$$

Trotter and Gleser (1952) corrected each cadaver length measurement in their Terry Collection sample for changes due to aging, and only then computed the regressions. The regression formulae in their study, therefore, compute stature for 30-year-old individuals. In the present study, cadaver length was not corrected for aging effects. As a consequence, the regression formulae in Tables XLVIII-L yield stature estimates for individuals that are of the same age as the mean age of the samples used in the derivation.

If it is known or suspected that the incomplete bone under study is from an individual who was younger, or older, than the mean age of the sample used in the present study, it is possible to correct the stature estimate for the changes due to the age difference. The basic correction formula is supplied by Trotter and Gleser (1952); namely, $0.06(\text{age} - 30)$. In order to proceed, the word "age" in this formula must be replaced by a figure. This means that the incomplete bone, for which stature is being estimated, must be assigned an age, either known or assumed. This assigned age, however, is not used directly in the formula. Instead, this part of the formula is changed to take into account the difference between the mean age of the present sample and age 30. This change results in the following formula:

$$0.06[(\text{mean age of sample} - 30) - (\text{assumed age of individual} - 30)]$$

Thus, continuing with the example being used (a Negro male estimated to have a stature of 170.99 ± 3.72 cm), and assigning him an age of 35, the stature correction for age is computed as follows:

$$43.25 - 30 = 13.25$$
$$35.00 - 30 = \underline{5.00}$$
$$8.25$$
$$\times \underline{.06}$$
$$.4950 \text{ cm.}$$

Since the age assigned in this case is below the mean age of the sample, but older than 30 years, the above product is added to the score. If the assigned age had been greater than the mean age of the sample, the above product would have been subtracted. The estimated stature by my formula, therefore, becomes 171.48 ± 3.72 cm.

Discussion

It will have been noticed that, in the hypothetical case of the femur fragment from the 35-year-old male Negro, different stature estimates were obtained by the two methods described herein. By the first method of estimating total bone length from the fragment, and then applying the result in the appropriate formula of Trotter and Gleser, I obtained a figure of 173.34 ± 5.33 cm. This has still to be corrected for age; $0.06(35-30) = 0.3$ cm. The estimate is thereby reduced to 173.04 ± 5.33 cm. On the other hand, by the (second) method of estimating stature directly from the fragment, I obtained an age-corrected estimate of 171.48 ± 3.72 cm. The difference is 1.56 cm.

The reason for the lack of agreement is that two different samples were employed to establish the regression formulae used to make the indirect estimate: the Terry Collection for the formula (mine) used in the total bone length estimate, and the military personnel of World War II for the formula (Trotter and Gleser) used in the stature estimate. In the case of the stature estimate made directly from the fragment, both formulae are based on the Terry Collection. Tests have convinced me that these sample differences largely account for the variations in stature estimates such as this sample illustrates. I have found the differences in stature estimates by the two methods to be greatest in White males, least in White females, and intermediate in Negro females and Negro males, in that order.

The use of skeletal samples from earlier times, which cannot be avoided in studies of this sort, brings up the problem of increasing stature in the American population. Trotter and Gleser (1958) pointed out that their sample from the Korean War shows a higher stature than their samples from World War II and the Terry Collection. If this indicates a continuation in the secular trend, regression formulae that are based on the earlier samples will probably somewhat underestimate the stature of a more recent sample. Because of the fluctuation in the relationship of long bone length to stature, the major emphasis in the present paper is on the estimation of maximum long bone length. This means, of course, that a second operation is required to convert the bone length into stature. Although some may object to the two-step method, on the grounds that it increases the standard error of the estimate, I regard it as the more realistic one until regressions between segments and stature can be based on current samples.

TABLE XXX
Means ($\pm$ One Standard Deviation) of the Lengths (in cm) of the Four Segments of the Femur, by Race and Sex.

Femur segment	White males M	White males s.d.	Negro males M	Negro males s.d.	White females M	White females s.d.	Negro females M	Negro females s.d.
1	8.06	0.79	8.08	0.60	7.11	0.62	7.15	0.63
2	27.13	2.31	28.34	2.17	25.45	2.13	26.23	1.74
3	7.12	1.05	7.51	1.32	6.51	0.79	6.88	0.90
4	3.90	0.28	3.93	0.22	3.55	0.28	3.64	0.27

TABLE XXXI

**Means (± One Standard Deviation) of the Lengths (in cm) of the
Five Segments of the Tibia, by Race and Sex.**

Tibia segment	White males M	White males s.d.	Negro males M	Negro males s.d.	White females M	White females s.d.	Negro females M	Negro females s.d.
1	3.20	0.43	3.23	0.34	2.85	0.33	2.74	0.36
2	6.67	0.87	6.85	1.00	5.99	0.84	6.08	0.93
3	16.35	1.59	18.06	1.86	15.98	1.24	17.31	1.55
4	10.09	1.27	11.15	1.57	8.72	1.02	9.31	1.11
5	1.43	0.23	1.45	0.20	1.32	0.22	1.35	0.17

TABLE XXXII

**Means (± One Standard Deviation) of the Lengths (in cm) of the
Four Segments of the Humerus, by Race and Sex.**

Humerus segment	White males M	White males s.d.	Negro males M	Negro males s.d.	White females M	White females s.d.	Negro females M	Negro females s.d.
1	3.74	0.26	3.83	0.26	3.26	0.20	3.29	0.20
2	25.33	1.73	26.64	1.61	23.66	1.53	23.93	1.32
3	2.03	0.26	1.99	0.28	1.77	0.20	1.83	0.22
4	1.75	0.19	1.74	0.17	1.49	0.17	1.61	0.18

TABLE XXXIII

**Correlations of Femur Segment(s) Length with Maximum Bone Length and
with Stature, by Race and Sex.**

Femur segment(s)	White Males Maximum Length	White Males Stature	Negro Males Maximum Length	Negro Males Stature	White Females Maximum Length	White Females Stature	Negro Females Maximum Length	Negro Females Stature
1	0.651	0.602	0.606	0.472	0.623	0.498	0.543	0.431
2	0.857	0.747	0.881	0.802	0.927	0.770	0.820	0.508
3	0.366	0.345	0.696	0.664	0.315	0.163	0.458	0.203
4	0.551	0.891	0.427	0.330	0.423	0.438	0.464	0.337
1+2	0.922	—	0.926	—	0.951	—	0.907	—
2+3	0.956	0.845	0.980	0.907	0.974	0.785	0.944	0.549
3+4	0.617	—	0.747	—	0.495	—	0.568	—
1+2+3	0.988	0.882	0.989	0.910	0.996	0.799	0.995	0.592
2+3+4	0.970	0.880	0.998	0.909	0.977	0.803	0.970	0.629

TABLE XXXIV

**Correlations of Tibia Segment(s) Length with Maximum Length and
Stature, by Race and Sex.**

Tibia segment(s)	White Males Maximum Length	White Males Stature	Negro Males Maximum Length	Negro Males Stature	White Females Maximum Length	White Females Stature	Negro Females Maximum Length	Negro Females Stature
1	0.320	0.339	0.219	0.176	0.297	0.236	0.173	0.212
2	0.492	0.480	0.523	0.435	0.629	0.576	0.596	0.431
3	0.687	0.578	0.659	0.532	0.658	0.515	0.551	0.429
4	0.633	0.490	0.676	0.689	0.704	0.549	0.555	0.330
5	0.228	0.078	0.304	0.165	0.410	0.235	0.086	0.085
1+2	0.595	—	0.539	—	0.642	—	0.599	—
2+3	0.855	—	0.830	—	0.909	—	0.877	—
3+4	0.922	—	0.925	—	0.901	—	0.888	—
4+5	0.710	—	0.705	—	0.751	—	0.582	—
1+2+3	0.881	—	0.854	—	0.918	—	0.880	—
2+3+4	0.980	0.832	0.991	0.893	0.984	0.811	0.980	0.700
3+4+5	0.930	0.749	0.936	0.853	0.914	0.704	0.896	0.620
1+2+3+4	0.995	0.862	0.998	0.896	0.989	0.813	0.995	0.727
2+3+4+5	0.986	0.833	0.994	0.894	0.986	0.813	0.988	0.707

TABLE XXXV

Correlations of Humerus Segment(s) Length with Maximum Length and with Stature, by Race and Sex.

Humerus segment(s)	White Males		Negro Males		White Females		Negro Females	
	Maximum Length	Stature	Maximum Length	Stature	Maximum Length	Stature	Maximum Length	Stature
1	0.472	0.475	0.469	0.515	0.550	0.355	0.370	0.395
2	0.981	0.749	0.978	0.782	0.968	0.741	0.965	0.629
3	0.359	0.380	0.187	0.083	0.459	0.250	0.346	0.322
4	0.533	0.406	0.116	0.137	0.299	0.424	0.447	0.190
1+2	0.990	0.782	0.987	0.824	0.985	0.774	0.982	0.647
2+3	0.986	0.772	0.985	0.783	0.974	0.746	0.981	0.642
3+4	0.636	—	0.240	—	0.538	—	0.559	—
1+2+3	0.997	0.810	0.994	0.824	0.990	0.776	0.992	0.647
2+3+4	0.993	0.779	0.988	0.789	0.990	0.778	0.988	0.656

TABLE XXXVI

Regression Formulae for the Calculation of Maximum Length and Standard Error (in cm) of the FEMUR from One or More of its Segments: White Males.

$0.65(Fem.1) + 40.91 = $ maximum length $\pm$ 2.32 cm.

$0.86(Fem.2) + 22.91 = $ maximum length $\pm$ 1.57 cm.

$3.66(Fem.3) + 20.10 = $ maximum length $\pm$ 2.84 cm.

$5.51(Fem.4) + 24.66 = $ maximum length $\pm$ 2.55 cm.

$1.42(Fem.1) + 0.93(Fem.2) + 9.51 = $ maximum length $\pm$ 1.20 cm.

$1.16(Fem.2) + 1.22(Fem.3) + 6.01 = $ maximum length $\pm$ 0.91 cm.

$0.81(Fem.3) + 5.47(Fem.4) + 19.05 = $ maximum length $\pm$ 2.42 cm.

$1.07(Fem.1) + 1.01(Fem.2) + 1.06(Fem.3) + 2.61 = $ maximum length $\pm$ 0.48 cm.

$1.07(Fem.2) + 1.12(Fem.3) + 1.99(Fem.4) + 1.48 = $ maximum length $\pm$ 0.76 cm.

TABLE XXXVII

Regression Formulae for the Calculation of Maximum Length and Standard Error (in cm) of the FEMUR from One or More of its Segments: Negro Males.

$0.61(Fem.1) + 42.96 = $ maximum length $\pm$ 2.66 cm.

$0.88(Fem.2) + 22.89 = $ maximum length $\pm$ 1.58 cm.

$0.70(Fem.3) + 42.63 = $ maximum length $\pm$ 2.40 cm.

$4.27(Fem.4) + 31.08 = $ maximum length $\pm$ 3.02 cm.

$1.70(Fem.1) + 1.15(Fem.2) + 1.46 = $ maximum length $\pm$ 1.28 cm.

$1.12(Fem.2) + 1.13(Fem.3) + 7.92 = $ maximum length $\pm$ 0.67 cm.

$1.57(Fem.3) + 4.11(Fem.4) + 19.89 = $ maximum length $\pm$ 2.25 cm.

$1.16(Fem.1) + 1.01(Fem.2) + 1.01(Fem.3) + 2.33 = $ maximum length $\pm$ 0.20 cm.

$1.06(Fem.2) + 1.08(Fem.3) + 2.00(Fem.4) + 1.75 = $ maximum length $\pm$ 0.52 cm.

TABLE XXXVIII

Regression Formulae for the Calculation of Maximum Length and Standard Error (in cm) of the FEMUR from One or More of its Segments: White Females.

$0.62(Fem.1) + 38.21 = $ maximum length $\pm$ 2.15 cm.

$0.93(Fem.2) + 19.05 = $ maximum length $\pm$ 1.03 cm.

$3.15(Fem.3) + 22.15 = $ maximum length $\pm$ 2.60 cm.

$4.23(Fem.4) + 27.63 = $ maximum length $\pm$ 2.49 cm.

$1.04(Fem.1) + 1.04(Fem.2) + 8.80 = $ maximum length $\pm$ 0.86 cm.

$1.17(Fem.2) + 1.02(Fem.3) + 6.14 = $ maximum length $\pm$ 0.63 cm.

$0.89(Fem.3) + 3.70(Fem.4) + 23.71 = $ maximum length $\pm$ 2.41 cm.

$1.04(Fem.1) + 1.03(Fem.2) + 1.02(Fem.3) + 2.38 = $ maximum length $\pm$ 0.25 cm.

$1.14(Fem.2) + 0.98(Fem.3) + 0.78(Fem.4) + 4.49 = $ maximum length $\pm$ 0.60 cm.

TABLE XXXIX
Regression Formulae for the Calculation of Maximum Length and Standard Error (in cm) of the FEMUR from One or More of its Segments: Negro Females.

0.54(Fem.1) + 40.00 = maximum length ± 1.95 cm.

0.82(Fem.2) + 22.38 = maximum length ± 1.33 cm.

4.58(Fem.3) + 12.38 = maximum length ± 2.07 cm.

4.64(Fem.4) + 27.01 = maximum length ± 2.06 cm.

1.44(Fem.1) + 0.98(Fem.2) + 7.89 = maximum length ± 0.98 cm.

1.09(Fem.2) + 1.19(Fem.3) + 7.02 = maximum length ± 0.78 cm.

0.88(Fem.3) + 3.03(Fem.4) + 26.82 = maximum length ± 1.93 cm.

1.18(Fem.1) + 1.01(Fem.2) + 1.06(Fem.3) + 1.75 = maximum length ± 0.24 cm.

1.05(Fem.2) + 1.00(Fem.3) + 2.07(Fem.4) + 1.93 = maximum length ± 0.57 cm.

TABLE XL
Regression Formulae for the Calculation of Maximum Length and Standard Error (in cm) of the TIBIA from One or More of its Segments: White Males.

3.20(Tib.1) + 27.48 = maximum length ± 2.42 cm.

4.92(Tib.2) + 4.90 = maximum length ± 2.22 cm.

0.69(Tib.3) + 26.49 = maximum length ± 1.86 cm.

0.63(Tib.4) + 31.33 = maximum length ± 1.98 cm.

2.28(Tib.5) + 34.46 = maximum length ± 2.49 cm.

1.95(Tib.1) + 1.46(Tib.2) + 21.71 = maximum length ± 2.08 cm.

1.48(Tib.2) + 1.11(Tib.3) + 9.71 = maximum length ± 1.34 cm.

1.06(Tib.3) + 1.23(Tib.4) + 7.96 = maximum length ± 1.00 cm.

1.36(Tib.4) + 3.59(Tib.5) + 19.04 = maximum length ± 1.82 cm.

1.27(Tib.1) + 1.50(Tib.2) + 1.05(Tib.3) + 6.54 = maximum length ± 1.24 cm.

1.02(Tib.2) + 1.08(Tib.3) + 1.01(Tib.4) + 3.06 = maximum length ± 0.52 cm.

1.00(Tib.3) + 1.27(Tib.4) + 1.38(Tib.5) + 6.61 = maximum length ± 0.96 cm.

1.02(Tib.1) + 1.05(Tib.2) + 1.03(Tib.3) + 0.98(Tib.4) + 0.71 = maximum length ± 0.26 cm.

1.01(Tib.2) + 1.03(Tib.3) + 1.04(Tib.4) + 1.21(Tib.5) + 1.95 = maximum length ± 0.44 cm.

TABLE XLI
Regression Formulae for the Calculation of Maximum Length and Standard Error (in cm) of the TIBIA from One or More of its Segments: Negro Males.

2.19(Tib.1) + 33.68 = maximum length ± 2.93 cm.

5.23(Tib.2) + 4.92 = maximum length ± 2.54 cm.

0.66(Tib.3) + 28.85 = maximum length ± 2.24 cm.

0.68(Tib.4) + 33.21 = maximum length ± 2.19 cm.

3.04(Tib.5) + 36.34 = maximum length ± 2.83 cm.

1.12(Tib.1) + 1.48(Tib.2) + 26.98 = maximum length ± 2.55 cm.

1.49(Tib.2) + 1.02(Tib.3) + 12.14 = maximum length ± 1.69 cm.

1.00(Tib.3) + 1.22(Tib.4) + 9.14 = maximum length ± 1.15 cm.

1.21(Tib.4) + 3.08(Tib.5) + 22.83 = maximum length ± 2.14 cm.

1.78(Tib.1) + 1.38(Tib.2) + 1.06(Tib.3) + 6.47 = maximum length ± 1.59 cm.

1.08(Tib.2) + 0.99(Tib.3) + 1.05(Tib.4) + 3.80 = maximum length ± 0.42 cm.

0.98(Tib.3) + 1.18(Tib.4) + 2.19(Tib.5) + 6.82 = maximum length ± 1.08 cm.

1.08(Tib.1) + 1.03(Tib.2) + 1.01(Tib.3) + 1.01(Tib.4) + 0.66 = maximum length ± 0.20 cm.

1.04(Tib.2) + 0.98(Tib.3) + 1.03(Tib.4) + 1.24(Tib.5) + 2.70 = maximum length ± 0.35 cm.

TABLE XLII
Regression Formulae for the Calculation of Maximum Length and Standard Error (in cm) of the TIBIA from One or More of its Segments: White Females.

2.97(Tib.1) + 26.43 = maximum length ± 2.15 cm.

0.63(Tib.2) + 31.12 = maximum length ± 1.75 cm.

0.66(Tib.3) + 24.38 = maximum length ± 1.69 cm.

0.70(Tib.4) + 28.75 = maximum length ± 1.60 cm.

4.10(Tib.5) + 29.48 = maximum length ± 2.05 cm.

0.89(Tib.1) + 1.57(Tib.2) + 22.94 = maximum length ± 1.74 cm.

1.66(Tib.2) + 1.18(Tib.3) + 6.10 = maximum length ± 0.95 cm.

1.02(Tib.3) + 1.36(Tib.4) + 6.74 = maximum length ± 0.99 cm.

1.41(Tib.4) + 2.78(Tib.5) + 18.92 = maximum length ± 1.50 cm.

0.92(Tib.1) + 1.56(Tib.2) + 1.18(Tib.3) + 4.05 = maximum length ± 0.91 cm.

1.17(Tib.2) + 1.07(Tib.3) + 0.93(Tib.4) + 2.71 = maximum length ± 0.41 cm.

0.96(Tib.3) + 1.29(Tib.4) + 1.66(Tib.5) + 6.02 = maximum length ± 0.93 cm.

0.70(Tib.1) + 1.10(Tib.2) + 1.07(Tib.3) + 0.91(Tib.4) + 1.22 = maximum length ± 0.34 cm.

1.12(Tib.2) + 1.04(Tib.3) + 0.91(Tib.4) + 0.75(Tib.5) + 2.55 = maximum length ± 0.39 cm.

TABLE XLIII

Regression Formulae for the Calculation of Maximum Length and Standard Error (in cm) of the TIBIA from One or More of its Segments: Negro Females.

1.73(Tib.1) + 32.03 = maximum length ± 2.08 cm.
5.96(Tib.2) + 5.33 = maximum length ± 1.70 cm.
0.55(Tib.3) + 27.33 = maximum length ± 1.76 cm.
0.56(Tib.4) + 31.60 = maximum length ± 1.76 cm.
8.60(Tib.5) + 25.16 = maximum length ± 2.10 cm.
0.34(Tib.1) + 1.32(Tib.2) + 27.85 = maximum length ± 1.71 cm.
1.55(Tib.2) + 0.88(Tib.3) + 12.08 = maximum length ± 1.02 cm.
0.96(Tib.3) + 1.35(Tib.4) + 7.48 = maximum length ± 0.98 cm.
1.10(Tib.4) + 2.23(Tib.5) + 23.48 = maximum length ± 1.73 cm.
0.41(Tib.1) + 1.52(Tib.2) + 0.88(Tib.3) + 11.11 = maximum length ± 1.02 cm.
1.05(Tib.2) + 0.99(Tib.3) + 0.95(Tib.4) + 4.36 = maximum length ± 0.42 cm.
0.95(Tib.3) + 1.38(Tib.4) + 1.48(Tib.5) + 5.45 = maximum length ± 0.96 cm.
1.03(Tib.1) + 0.93(Tib.2) + 1.00(Tib.3) + 1.03(Tib.4) + 1.26 = maximum length ± 0.23 cm.
1.06(Tib.2) + 0.98(Tib.3) + 0.98(Tib.4) + 1.57(Tib.5) + 2.19 = maximum length ± 0.34 cm.

TABLE XLIV

Regression Formulae for the Calculation of Maximum Length and Standard Error (in cm) of the HUMERUS from One or More of its Segments: White Males.

4.72(Hum.1) + 15.20 = maximum length ± 1.80 cm.
0.98(Hum.2) + 8.00 = maximum length ± 0.40 cm.
3.59(Hum.3) + 25.56 = maximum length ± 1.91 cm.
5.33(Hum.4) + 23.52 = maximum length ± 1.73 cm.
1.08(Hum.1) + 1.09(Hum.2) + 1.32 = maximum length ± 0.29 cm.
1.11(Hum.2) + 0.82(Hum.3) + 3.03 = maximum length ± 0.34 cm.
2.72(Hum.3) + 5.49(Hum.4) + 17.71 = maximum length ± 1.59 cm.
1.17(Hum.1) + 1.04(Hum.2) + 0.94(Hum.3) + 0.14 = maximum length ± 0.17 cm.
1.04(Hum.2) + 0.93(Hum.3) + 1.35(Hum.4) + 2.27 = maximum length ± 0.25 cm.

TABLE XLV

Regression Formulae for the Calculation of Maximum Length and Standard Error (in cm) of the HUMERUS from One or More of its Segments: Negro Males.

4.69(Hum.1) + 16.27 = maximum length ± 1.57 cm.
0.98(Hum.2) + 8.18 = maximum length ± 0.37 cm.
1.87(Hum.3) + 30.51 = maximum length ± 1.74 cm.
1.16(Hum.4) + 32.21 = maximum length ± 1.00 cm.
0.95(Hum.1) + 1.01(Hum.2) + 3.73 = maximum length ± 0.28 cm.
1.05(Hum.2) + 0.71(Hum.3) + 4.76 = maximum length ± 0.31 cm.
1.32(Hum.3) + 1.55(Hum.4) + 28.90 = maximum length ± 1.74 cm.
0.94(Hum.1) + 1.00(Hum.2) + 0.69(Hum.3) + 2.62 = maximum length ± 0.21 cm.
1.05(Hum.2) + 0.80(Hum.3) + 0.84(Hum.4) + 3.28 = maximum length ± 0.28 cm.

TABLE XLVI

Regression Formulae for the Calculation of Maximum Length and Standard Error (in cm) of the HUMERUS from One or More of its Segments: White Females.

5.50(Hum.1) + 12.58 = maximum length ± 1.60 cm.
0.97(Hum.2) + 7.57 = maximum length ± 0.45 cm.
4.59(Hum.3) + 22.28 = maximum length ± 1.62 cm.
2.99(Hum.4) + 25.87 = maximum length ± 1.54 cm.
1.66(Hum.1) + 1.04(Hum.2) + 0.20 = maximum length ± 0.30 cm.
1.04(Hum.2) + 1.12(Hum.3) + 3.47 = maximum length ± 0.40 cm.
2.60(Hum.3) + 4.17(Hum.4) + 19.77 = maximum length ± 1.47 cm.
1.53(Hum.1) + 1.01(Hum.2) + 0.87(Hum.3) − 0.37 = maximum length ± 0.25 cm.
0.99(Hum.2) + 1.05(Hum.3) + 1.85(Hum.4) + 2.16 = maximum length ± 0.25 cm.

TABLE XLVII

Regression Formulae for the Calculation of Maximum Length and Standard Error (in cm) of the HUMERUS from One or More of its Segments: Negro Females.

$3.70(Hum.1) + 18.12 = $ maximum length $\pm$ 1.30 cm.
$0.96(Hum.2) + 7.35 = $ maximum length $\pm$ 0.39 cm.
$3.46(Hum.3) + 24.06 = $ maximum length $\pm$ 1.39 cm.
$4.47(Hum.4) + 23.52 = $ maximum length $\pm$ 1.49 cm.
$1.40(Hum.1) + 1.04(Hum.2) + 1.12 = $ maximum length $\pm$ 0.30 cm.
$1.07(Hum.2) + 1.16(Hum.3) + 2.98 = $ maximum length $\pm$ 0.31 cm.
$3.29(Hum.3) + 2.74(Hum.4) + 20.25 = $ maximum length $\pm$ 1.31 cm.
$1.25(Hum.1) + 1.00(Hum.2) + 1.01(Hum.3) + 0.86 = $ maximum length $\pm$ 0.20 cm.
$1.03(Hum.2) + 1.27(Hum.3) + 1.10(Hum.4) + 1.88 = $ maximum length $\pm$ 0.24 cm.

TABLE XLVIII

Regression Formulae for Calculating Living Stature and Standard Error (in cm) from an Incomplete FEMUR (See Text for Correction for Loss in Stature from Aging)

WHITE MALES   MEAN AGE = 52.97
$2.71(Fem.2) + 3.06(Fem.3) + 73.00 = $ stature $\pm$ 4.41 cm.
$2.89(Fem.1) + 2.31(Fem.2) + 2.62(Fem.3) + 63.88 = $ stature $\pm$ 3.93 cm.
$2.35(Fem.2) + 2.65(Fem.3) + 7.92(Fem.4) + 54.97 = $ stature $\pm$ 3.95 cm.

NEGRO MALES   MEAN AGE = 43.25
$2.59(Fem.2) + 2.91(Fem.3) + 75.74 = $ stature $\pm$ 3.72 cm.
$1.20(Fem.1) + 2.48(Fem.2) + 2.78(Fem.3) + 69.94 = $ stature $\pm$ 3.71 cm.
$2.53(Fem.2) + 2.84(Fem.3) + 2.40(Fem.4) + 68.32 = $ stature $\pm$ 3.72 cm.

WHITE FEMALES   MEAN AGE = 63.35
$2.80(Fem.2) + 1.46(Fem.3) + 76.67 = $ stature $\pm$ 4.91 cm.
$2.16(Fem.1) + 2.50(Fem.2) + 1.45(Fem.3) + 68.86 = $ stature $\pm$ 4.81 cm.
$2.57(Fem.2) + 1.21(Fem.3) + 5.03(Fem.4) + 66.05 = $ stature $\pm$ 4.77 cm.

NEGRO FEMALES   MEAN AGE = 39.58
$2.12(Fem.2) + 1.68(Fem.3) + 93.29 = $ stature $\pm$ 6.17 cm.
$3.63(Fem.1) + 1.86(Fem.2) + 1.27(Fem.3) + 77.15 = $ stature $\pm$ 5.80 cm.
$2.00(Fem.2) + 1.08(Fem.3) + 6.32(Fem.4) + 77.71 = $ stature $\pm$ 6.01 cm.

TABLE XLIX

Regression Formulae for Calculating Living Stature and Standard Error (in cm) from an Incomplete TIBIA (See Text for Correction for Loss in Stature from Aging)

WHITE MALES   MEAN AGE = 52.97
$3.52(Tib.2) + 2.89(Tib.3) + 2.23(Tib.4) + 74.55 = $ stature $\pm$ 4.56 cm.
$2.87(Tib.3) + 2.96(Tib.4) - 0.96(Tib.5) + 92.36 = $ stature $\pm$ 5.45 cm.
$4.19(Tib.1) + 3.63(Tib.2) + 2.69(Tib.3) + 2.10(Tib.4) + 64.95 = $ stature $\pm$ 4.22 cm.
$3.54(Tib.2) + 2.96(Tib.3) + 2.18(Tib.4) - 1.56(Tib.5) + 75.98 = $ stature $\pm$ 4.60 cm.

NEGRO MALES   MEAN AGE = 43.25
$2.26(Tib.2) + 2.22(Tib.3) + 3.17(Tib.4) + 5.86 = $ stature $\pm$ 3.88 cm.
$2.23(Tib.3) + 3.51(Tib.4) + 0.51(Tib.5) + 91.70 = $ stature $\pm$ 4.49 cm.
$1.79(Tib.1) + 2.18(Tib.2) + 2.25(Tib.3) + 3.10(Tib.4) + 75.87 = $ stature $\pm$ 3.88 cm.
$2.32(Tib.2) + 2.23(Tib.3) + 3.19(Tib.4) - 1.60(Tib.5) + 82.50 = $ stature $\pm$ 3.92 cm.

WHITE FEMALES   MEAN AGE = 63.35
$4.17(Tib.2) + 2.96(Tib.3) + 2.16(Tib.4) + 66.09 = $ stature $\pm$ 4.69 cm.
$2.75(Tib.3) + 3.65(Tib.4) + 1.17(Tib.5) + 79.92 = $ stature $\pm$ 5.69 cm.
$1.51(Tib.1) + 4.03(Tib.2) + 2.97(Tib.3) + 2.12(Tib.4) + 62.89 = $ stature $\pm$ 4.71 cm.
$4.31(Tib.2) + 3.05(Tib.3) + 2.20(Tib.4) - 2.34(Tib.5) + 66.60 = $ stature $\pm$ 4.72 cm.

NEGRO FEMALES   MEAN AGE = 39.58
$2.56(Tib.2) + 2.21(Tib.3) + 1.56(Tib.4) + 91.91 = $ stature $\pm$ 4.59 cm.
$2.11(Tib.3) + 2.61(Tib.4) + 3.58(Tib.5) + 94.57 = $ stature $\pm$ 5.04 cm.
$3.60(Tib.1) + 2.15(Tib.2) + 2.26(Tib.3) + 1.84(Tib.4) + 81.11 = $ stature $\pm$ 4.46 cm.
$2.58(Tib.2) + 2.17(Tib.3) + 1.63(Tib.4) + 3.80(Tib.5) + 86.64 = $ stature $\pm$ 4.59 cm.

TABLE L

Regression Formulae for Calculating Living Stature and Standard Error (in cm) from an Incomplete HUMERUS (See text for Correction for Loss in Stature from Aging)

WHITE MALES   MEAN AGE = 52.97

3.42(Hum.2) + 80.94 = stature ± 5.31 cm.
7.17(Hum.1) + 3.04(Hum.2) + 63.94 = stature ± 5.05 cm.
3.19(Hum.2) + 5.97(Hum.3) + 74.82 = stature ± 5.15 cm.
7.84(Hum.1) + 2.73(Hum.2) + 6.74(Hum.3) + 55.45 = stature ± 4.80 cm.
2.94(Hum.2) + 6.34(Hum.3) + 4.60(Hum.4) + 72.54 = stature ± 5.14 cm.

NEGRO MALES   MEAN AGE = 43.25

3.80(Hum.2) + 70.68 = stature ± 4.94 cm.
8.13(Hum.1) + 3.34(Hum.2) + 51.98 = stature ± 4.56 cm.
3.79(Hum.2) + 0.69(Hum.3) + 69.53 = stature ± 5.00 cm.
8.12(Hum.1) + 3.33(Hum.2) + 0.56(Hum.3) + 51.08 = stature ± 4.62 cm.
3.76(Hum.2) + 1.19(Hum.3) + 4.54(Hum.4) + 61.58 = stature ± 5.00 cm.

WHITE FEMALES   MEAN AGE = 63.35

3.87(Hum.2) + 66.14 = stature ± 5.40 cm.
8.84(Hum.1) + 3.65(Hum.2) + 42.43 = stature ± 5.14 cm.
3.77(Hum.2) + 3.35(Hum.3) + 62.59 = stature ± 5.42 cm.
8.55(Hum.1) + 3.60(Hum.2) + 1.93(Hum.3) + 41.16 = stature ± 5.18 cm.
3.44(Hum.2) + 2.92(Hum.3) + 10.84(Hum.4) + 54.91 = stature ± 5.16 cm.

NEGRO FEMALES   MEAN AGE = 39.58

2.95(Hum.2) + 89.15 = stature ± 4.88 cm.
5.05(Hum.1) + 2.64(Hum.2) + 80.13 = stature ± 4.83 cm.
2.75(Hum.2) + 3.76(Hum.3) + 87.08 = stature ± 4.85 cm.
4.54(Hum.1) + 2.50(Hum.2) + 3.19(Hum.3) + 79.29 = stature ± 4.82 cm.
2.66(Hum.2) + 4.03(Hum.3) + 2.83(Hum.4) + 84.25 = stature ± 4.87 cm.

Literature Cited

Genovés T., Santiago
1967. Proportionality of the Long Bones and Their Relation to Stature in Mesoamericans. *American Journal of Physical Anthropology*, new series, 26: 67-78.
Müller, Gertrude
1935. Zur Bestimmung der Länge beschädigter Extremitätenknochen. *Anthropologischer Anzeiger.* 12: 70-2.
Steele, D. G., and McKern, T. W.
1969. A Method for Assessment of Maximum Long Bone Length and Living Stature from Fragmentary Long Bones. *American Journal of Physical Anthropology*, 31: 215-227.
Terry, R. J.
1940. On Measuring and Photographing the Cadaver. *American Journal of Physical Anthropology*, 26: 433-47.
Trotter, M., and Gleser, G. C.
1951. The Effect of Ageing on Stature. *American Journal of Physical Anthropology*, new series, 9: 311-24.
1952. Estimation of Stature from Long Bones of American Whites and Negroes. *American Journal of Physical Anthropology*, new series. 9: 427-40.
1958. A Re-evaluation of Estimation of Stature Based on Measurements of Stature Taken During Life and of Long Bones After Death. *American Journal of Physical Anthropology*, new series, 16: 78-123.

Discriminant Function Sexing of The Human Skeleton

Eugene Giles

To the anthropologist, the problem of identification is usually one of establishing the demographic characteristics of a skeletal population. This is not to say, of course, that a physical anthropologist cannot apply his knowledge to a single specimen, perhaps the victim of a crime, in order to provide certain desired information. It merely means that his professional interest in identification is focused on some *population,* for which he hopes he has, in his laboratory, a representative sample, and from which he can adduce such features as sex, race, age, stature, body form, disease as reflected in the bone, and the like. In dealing with specimens from a remote time or place, he is rarely even interested in the attributes of the individuals as such, but he employs the individual cases only to go on to broader conclusions that form a biological profile of the population from which the sample was drawn.

A natural development in the study of populations, not individuals, is the adoption and refinement of statistical methods in order to extract a pattern from an extravagance of evidence. As the science of physical anthropology established itself in the 19th century, it became apparent that there literally was almost no end to the measurements and observations that could be made on the human skeleton. Even the Hungarian anthropologist, Aurel von Török, famous for recommending over 5,000 measurements per skull, began to have second thoughts in the 1890s. What might be done with the accumulating piles of raw measurements and observations became a critical problem, for the data simply did not sort themselves out in any meaningful fashion.

Early in this century, Karl Pearson and his associates at University College, London, were faced with two problems in their investigations of the variation in human skulls. They often had small samples of crania from the same country or region, and wished to pool these, if appropriate, to form one large sample. They also realized that the morphology of the human skull was best represented by a number of measurements considered together, not one at a time. Pearson devised what was called the "Coefficient of Racial Likeness" to meet these difficulties. The CRL used several measurements, at one time, to assess the similarity of two samples, but certain theoretical objections eventually led to its abandonment. The CRL, however, as M. A. Girshick has noted (Hodges, 1955), represents the first, or Pearsonian, stage in the development of multivariate discriminatory analysis; the second, or Fisherian stage, evolved the specific statistical techniques currently in use.

Sir Ronald Fisher's multivariate linear discriminant analysis is best explained by resorting to a specific case. Suppose we wish to determine an individual's stature from his femur length. In such a case, it is customary to call stature the dependent variable and femur length the independent variable since, for these purposes, the man's stature estimation is dependent upon the numerical value of his femur's length. If y = stature and x = femur length, then what is called a simple regression equation, $y = a + bx$, is the means to predict stature from femur length. Here, a and b are the two numbers which, in the equation $y = a + bx$, give the best possible prediction of y from x. To make a predictive use of this regression formula requires that we first solve the equation for a and b. This is done by obtaining x and y values from a large and representative population where both variables can be measured. Then, when just a femur is available, an estimate of stature, y, can be made since a, b, and x are already known.

Multiple regression is the term applied when, instead of one dependent and one independent variable, there are two or more independent variables. In order to predict stature more accurately, we might, for example, wish to make use, not only of the femur's length, but also that of the tibia, radius, and humerus. Such an equation would have the form $y = b_1x_1 + b_2x_2 + b_3x_3 + b_4x_4$, where the x's represent the several independent variables. As before, to use this technique we first have to solve the equation, that is to say, we have to establish the values for b_1, b_2, b_3, and b_4 that provide the best possible prediction of stature.

Suppose, instead of stature, we wish to predict sex from skeletal measurements. In such a case, numbers like 0 for male and 1 for female, could represent the values to be assumed by the dependent variable y and a series of measurements x_1, x_2, x_3, etc., the independent variables. We now solve the multiple regression equation so that the values assigned b_1, b_2, b_3, etc. are chosen to best discriminate male and female on the basis of the measurements (x's). This means that, when measurements from males are entered into the equation, the value of y will go toward 0, while female measurements will make y approach 1. The means whereby the b values are determined, in order to provide the best possible separation of male and female, is beyond the scope of this paper (references and further description can be found in Cooley and Lohnes [1962]), but again a sample is required where both dependent (sex) and independent (skeletal measurements) variables are known.

Thus, the basic reasoning behind the discriminant function's determination of sex has been outlined. At this point, the questions might be raised, "Is the technique any good in sexing skeletal material? And, if so, is it practical?" The answer to both questions is, "Yes." A century ago the French anthropologist Dureau (1873) reviewed the techniques then in use for sexing crania and always found that about 10% could not be sexed. As many papers in the recent literature indicate, anthropologists' abilities have not improved at all since that time. Discriminant function sexing, to be sure, does no better, but it certainly does as well, as will be demonstrated in this paper. It also can be argued that the investigator who sexes by visual means considers much more information in his evaluation of a skull, particularly traits such as sharpness of orbital borders, which defy measurement and, therefore, his judgment is to be preferred to an impersonal, metrical method. Perhaps so, but if such acknowledged experts as Drs. T. D. Stewart and W. M. Krogman admit in print that they succeed during "blind tests" in identifying crania of known sex from dissecting rooms less than 90% of the time, why should other, less candid experts be accorded greater reliability? There is, moreover, no reason to believe this doubtful 10% shows up in forensic cases any less regularly than it does in anatomical laboratories.

As for the practicality of discriminant function sexing, the requirements are few. The actual calculation of the discriminant function is, of course, done on material of known sex. It only remains for the investigator to apply these results to his specimen(s), and this process is straightforward. In discriminant function analysis, the b values mentioned above, in connection with multiple regression, are called weights, the x's are the variables (skeletal measurements in this application), and y is called the score. An individual's discriminant function score is obtained simply by multiplying each measurement from a specimen by the appropriate weight and then summing. This score is then compared with a large number of scores obtained from specimens of known sex.

The scores from known-sex material fall into two groups that slightly overlap. A typical distribution of discriminant function scores for sexing crania is shown in

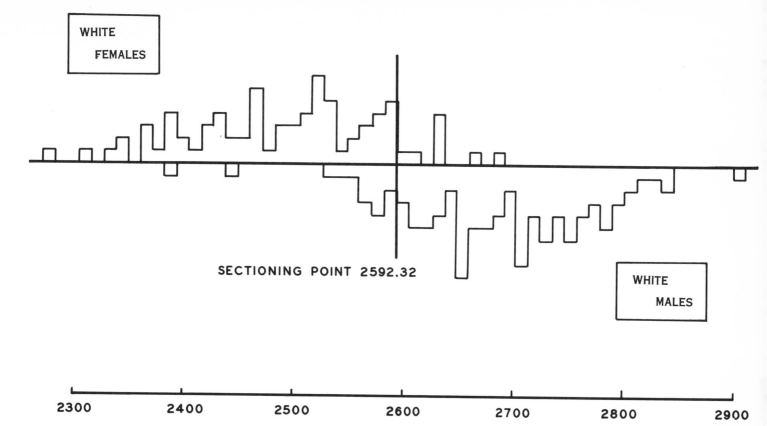

SECTIONING POINT 2592.32

2300   2400   2500   2600   2700   2800   2900

Figure 24. A sectioning point has been determined, which divides these scores into a male group and a female group, so that the minimum number of specimens is misclassified. If the specimen in question falls on the male side of this sectioning point, then it is deemed male; if on the other side, female.

Figure 24. The distribution of discriminant function scores for 187 White specimens —for Function Number 2 in table LI.

An example is in order. During the seminar, Dr. J. L. Angel permitted me to examine a human skull, which at that time was a piece of evidence under investigation by the FBI. The following measurements were recorded, in millimeters (see Appendix on page 00 for the definitions of the measurements):

Basion-nasion (4)	94
Maximum diameter bizygomatic (5)	125
Basion-prosthion (6)	93
Prosthion-nasion height (7)	72
Basion-bregma height (3)	128
Mastoid length (9)	29
Glabello-occipital length (1)	168
Maximum width (2)	140

In Table LI are discriminant functions for sexing crania. If we assume the specimen to be Caucasian, the above measurements are appropriate for discriminant function 2 in that table, i.e.:

$$3.400(168) - 3.833(140) + 5.433(128) - 0.167(94) + 12.200(125)$$
$$- 0.100(93) + 2.200(72) + 5.367(29) = 571.200 - 536.620 + 695.424$$
$$- 15.698 + 1525.000 - 9.300 + 158.400 + 155.643 = 2544.05$$

A score for this specimen of 2544 puts it on the female side of the sectioning point of 2592 but, as is clear from Figure 24, not far from the demarcation line. In fact, this skull, though small, had a number of the unmeasurable indicia of maleness, which presumably are reflected in the position of its discriminant function score relative to the majority of females. Whatever the skull's true sex, it serves to demonstrate the method by which a discriminant function is applied to a specimen in order to sex it.

Many such discriminant functions for sexing have been calculated for various populations, and using measurements on both the cranial and post-cranial skeleton.

Table LI, compiled from a number of research papers, has organized the published discriminant functions for crania into the three racial categories of American Negro, Caucasian, and Japanese. It is tempting to infer that these groups should, in fact, be considered to represent Negroid, Caucasoid, and Mongoloid peoples, but the author, while suspecting that such a generalization would be valid, is not prepared to state so without further testing on, say, Chinese and African populations. The functions for Caucasian crania, though based on an American White sample, have been found to produce equally good results when tested on French specimens of known sex (Boulinier, 1968), hence functions in this category are established on a wider basis. There is no indication that discriminant functions based on Japanese crania should be preferred in sexing American Indian specimens. In fact, Discriminant Function 12 in Table LI, based upon American Negroes, sexed a trial group of over 300 American Indian crania significantly more successfully (90.4% correct) than did either Discriminant Function 6 (85.9% correct) or 13 (85.3% correct).

Tables LI–LV have been organized, within each racial category, into discriminant functions that are applicable to the cranium, to the mandible, to the cranium plus mandible, to the post-cranial skeleton, and to the cranium plus post-cranial skeleton. All the information necessary to put the discriminant function technique into action is also supplied: name of measurement, discriminant function weights, sectioning point, and the percent of correct classification by the originator's estimation. Additional information is sometimes supplied by the original authors, such as the average score for each sex and the functions based on samples formed by combining two racial groups. If required, the probability of correct classification at various score values should be sought in the original papers.

What has been provided in Tables LI–LV is a fairly complete register of published discriminant functions for sexing skeletal material. These are all applied in the same way, and the example given above, for No. 2 in Table LI, can be used as a model. This paper's Appendix on page 108 provides appropriate definitions for each measurement; all measurements are in millimeters.

To sum up this introduction to discriminant function sexing of human skeletal material, it might be appropriate to indicate, from the forensic point of view, the pros and cons of the technique. First of all, it would be misleading to regard sexing by means of discriminant functions as being more accurate than that achieved by a well-trained physical anthropologist. Discriminant function sexing does not take into account any variables other than those that can normally be measured by spreading or sliding calipers. The advantage in using nonmetrical traits is problematical, however, since physical anthropologists seem to do no better when they use any or all of the visual clues they accept as valid. Of more practical concern is the inability of the discriminant functions now available to cope with specimens on which the designated complement of measurements cannot be taken. The difficulty of missing measurements, which result from fragmentary specimens, is partially alleviated by the availability of alternate functions that use different measurements, such as those provided by Giles and Elliot (1963) for American Negro and White crania.

Two other liabilities should be mentioned. First, it is decidedly helpful to have some prior knowledge of the race of the individual(s) to be sexed. This is often available or, in many cases, discriminant functions based on various racial samples will concur when they are used to sex a particular individual. Secondly, Boulinier (1969) and subsequently Giles (1970) have shown that in Giles' cranial sample of 408 American Negroes and Whites, where each specimen's age and sex are known from written records, the discriminant function method tends to misclassify younger males and older females. This is a tendency only; it would seem to have little practical effect and might, in fact, be present but undetected in visual sexing.

There also are a number of points that can be made on the positive side concerning the discriminant function technique, particularly with reference to this seminar on Personal Identification in Mass Disasters. No doubt an expert, if available, will be consulted for the occasional specimen that comes into the hands of say, the FBI, and properly so. Discriminant function methods, however, merit real consideration in the event of truly mass disasters. Technician-level personnel, with brief instructions in measuring, can perform discriminant function sexing quickly and without the need to consult any reference series of skeletal material. It is possible for the non-expert to establish, quite objectively, a level of certitude regarding the sex of any particular specimen merely by relating the discriminant function score to a published standard series. And, as it has been pointed out in this paper, when dealing with samples of reasonable size, the discriminant function method has the same overall accuracy in sexing as does the expert using the "eyeball" approach.

If sex identification becomes a problem in a mass disaster, it seems likely that physical anthropology experts may well be in short supply, to say nothing of getting them and the specimens together. In such an event, discriminant-function sexing might, in the process of identification, at the very least perform the role of triage, and so provide an initial identification in order to allow a better utilization of whatever personnel are available to carry out the work of individual ascertainment by such means as, say, dental idiosyncrasies.

TABLE LI
Discriminant Function Sexing by Cranial Measurements*

Measure-ment**	Caucasian						American Negro						Japanese	
	1	2	3	4	5	6	7	8	9	10	11	12	13	14
1	3.107	3.400	1.800		1.236	9.875	9.222	3.895	3.533		2.111	2.867	1.000	1.000
2	—4.643	—3.833	—1.783		—1.000		7.000	3.632	1.667		1.000		—0.062	0.221
3	5.786	5.433	2.767				1.000	1.000	0.867				1.865	
4		—0.167	—0.100	10.714		7.062		—2.053	0.100	1.000		—0.100		
5	14.821	12.200	6.300	16.381	3.291	19.062	31.111	12.947	8.700	19.389	4.963	12.367	1.257	1.095
6	1.000	—0.100		—1.000		—1.000	5.889	1.368		2.778		—0.233		
7	2.714	2.200		4.333		4.375	20.222	8.158		11.778		6.900		0.504
8	—5.179			—6.571			—30.556			—14.333				
9	6.071	5.367	2.833	14.810	1.528		47.111	19.947	14.367	23.667	8.037			
Section-ing point	2676.39	2592.32	1296.20	3348.27	536.93	5066.69	8171.53	4079.12	2515.91	3461.46	1387.72	2568.97	579.96	380.84
Percent correct	86.6	86.4	86.4	84.5	85.5	84.9	87.6	86.6	86.5	87.5	85.3	85.0	86.4	83.1

*See Appendix on page 108 for measurement description.

**Caucasian Discriminant Functions 1-6, and American Negro Functions 7-12 from Giles and Elliot (1963); Japanese Functions 13-14 from Hanihara (1959).

TABLE LII
Discriminant Function Sexing by Mandibular Measurements*

Measurement**	Caucasian			American Negro			Japanese
	1	2	3	4	5	6	7
10	1.390	22.206	2.862	1.065	2.020	3.892	2.235
11		—30.265			—2.292		
12		1.000	2.540		2.606	10.568	
13			—1.000			—9.027	
14			—5.954			—3.270	1.673
15			1.483			1.000	
16	2.304	19.708	5.172	2.105	3.076	10.486	2.949
17	1.000	7.360		1.000	1.000		1.000
Sectioning point	287.43	1960.05	524.79	265.74	549.82	1628.79	388.53
Percent correct	83.2	85.9	84.1	84.8	86.9	86.5	85.6

*See Appendix on page 108 for measurement description.

**Caucasian Discriminant Functions 1-3, and American Negro Functions 4-6 from Giles (1964); Japanese Discriminant Function 7 from Hanihara (1959).

TABLE LIII
Discriminant Function Sexing by Combined Cranial and Mandibular Measurements*

Measurement**	Japanese					American Negro
	1	2	3	4	5	6
1	1.000	1.000	1.000	1.000	1.000	1.289
3	2.614	2.519		2.560	2.271	
5	0.996	0.586	0.785	1.084	1.391	—0.100
7						1.489
9						4.289
10	2.364				2.708	—0.978
12						—0.544
16	2.055	2.713	1.981	2.604		3.478
17		0.661	0.404			1.400
Sectioning point	850.66	807.40	428.05	809.72	748.34	718.23
Percent correct	89.7	89.4	86.4	88.9	88.8	88.3

*See Appendix on page 108 for measurement description.

**Japanese Discriminant Functions 1-5 from Hanihara (1959); American Negro Function 6 from Giles (1970).

TABLE LIV
Discriminant Function Sexing by Post-cranial Measurements*

Measurement**	Caucasian				American Negro				Japanese			
	1R	2L	3	4	5	6	7	8	9R	10L	11R	12L
18	1.000	1.000			0.070	1.000	1.000	1.980			1.000	1.000
19	30.234	30.716			58.140	31.400	16.530				9.854	9.351
20	−3.535	−12.643									11.988	8.369
21	20.004	17.565									4.127	3.575
22				0.607	16.250	11.120	6.100	1.000				
23				−0.054	−63.640	−34.470	−13.800	−1.390				
24			−0.115	−0.099								
25			−0.182	−0.134								
26			0.828	0.451								
27			0.517	0.325								
28					2.680	2.450			1.000	1.000		
29					27.680	16.240			8.726	6.198		
30					16.090							
31									7.394	3.221		
Sectioning point	3040.32	2656.51	9.20	7.00	4099.00	1953.00	665.00	68.00	1189.51	804.28	1431.82	1277.83
Percent correct	94.4	94.3	93.1	96.5	98.5	97.5	96.9	93.5	92.9	93.6	96.2	95.9

Measurement**	Japanese											
	13R	14L	15R	16L	17R	18L	19R	20R	21R	22L	23L	24L
32	1.000	1.000										
33	1.917	1.273										
34	2.991	3.163										
35	9.126	7.711										
36			1.000	1.000								
37			8.068	6.501								
38			5.551	2.881								
39					1.000	1.000						
40					4.264	2.954						
41					7.544	5.605						
42					12.213	10.212						
43							1.000	1.000	1.000	1.000	1.000	1.000
44									1.350			1.494
45							6.335	1.899		1.929	1.846	
46							12.664	11.922	10.940	6.949	7.107	6.800
47							10.991			2.120		
Sectioning point	763.92	696.97	441.54	370.25	1802.10	1494.54	1660.16	782.10	634.75	669.79	611.03	508.35
Percent correct	96.7	97.0	88.9	90.5	95.7	95.3	96.8	96.0	95.6	94.8	94.7	94.1

*See Appendix on page 108 for measurement description; R and L indicate appropriate for right or left side.

**Caucasian Discriminant Functions 1-2 from Pons (1955), and 3-4 from Howells (1964); American Negro Functions 5-8 from Thieme (1957); Japanese Functions 9-24 from Hanihara (1958, 1959).

TABLE LV

Discriminant Function Sexing by Combined Cranial and Post-cranial Measurements*

Measure-ment**	Japanese						
	1	2	3	4	5	6	7
1	1.000			1.000	1.000	1.000	1.000
3		1.000	1.000				
18	0.107	0.031	0.176	0.138		0.220	
46	6.644	4.390		8.117	8.035		4.757
48	—5.050	—2.654	—3.281	—5.156	—5.586	—3.816	
49	2.678		2.090		2.152	2.491	2.124
Section-ing point	299.18	117.11	142.12	157.76	233.09	194.55	494.36
Percent correct	99.0	98.8	96.4	98.6	98.8	97.4	92.5

*See Appendix on page 00 for measurement description; right side used where choice exists.

**Japanese Discriminant Functions 1-7 from Hanihara et al. (1964).

Literature Cited

Boulinier, G.
1968. La détermination du sexe des crânes humains à l'aide des fonctions discriminantes. *Bulletins et Mémoires de le Société d'Anthropologie de Paris,* 12th series, 3:301-16.
1969. Variations avec l'âge du dimorphisme sexuel des crânes humains adultes: influence sur les possibilités de discrimination statistique des sujets. *Bulletins et Mémoires de la Société d'Anthropologie de Paris,* 12th series, 4:127-38.

Cooley, W. W. and Lohnes, P. R.
1962. *Multivariate Procedures for the Behavioral Sciences.* John Wiley, New York.
Dureau, A.
1873. Des caractères sexuels du crâne humain. *Revue d'Anthropologie,* 2: 475-487.
Giles, E.
1964. Sex Determination by Discriminant Function Analysis of the Mandible. *American Journal of Physical Anthropology,* 22: 129-135.

Giles, E.
1970. Sexing Crania by Discriminant Function Analysis: Effects of Age and Number of Variables. *Proceedings, VIIIth International Congress of Anthropological and Ethnological Sciences,* Tokyo, 1:59-61.
Giles, E. and Elliot, O.
1963. Sex Determination by Discriminant Function Analysis of Crania. *American Journal of Physical Anthropology,* 21: 53-68.
Hanihara, K.
1958. Sexual Diagnosis of Japanese Long Bones by Means of Discriminant Function. *Journal of the Anthropological Society of Nippon,* 66: 187-196. (In Japanese, with English summary.)

1959. Sex Diagnosis of Japanese Skulls and Scapulae by means of Discriminant Function. *Journal of the Anthropological Society of Nippon,* 67: 191-197. (In Japanese, with English summary.)
Hanihara, K.; Kimura, K.; and Minamidate, T.
1964. The Sexing of Japanese Skeletons by Means of Discriminant Function. *Japanese Journal of Legal Medicine,* 18: 107-114. (In Japanese, with English summary.)
Hodges, J. L.
1955. *Discriminatory Analysis:* I. Survey of Discriminatory Analysis. Project number 21-49-004, Report number 1, Air University School of Aviation Medicine, U.S. Air Force, Randolph Air Force Base, Texas.

Howells, W. W.
 1964. Détermination du sexe du bassin par fonction discriminante: étude de matériel du Docteur Gaillard. *Bulletins et Mémoires de la Société d'Anthropologie de Paris,* 11th series, 7: 95-105.
Pons, J.
 1955. The Sexual Diagnosis of Isolated Bones of the Skeleton. *Human Biology,* 27: 12-21.
Thieme, F. P.
 1957. Sex in Negro Skeletons. *Journal of Forensic Medicine,* 4: 72-81.

APPENDIX

Measurement Descriptions

1. Maximum length of the skull, from the most anterior point of the frontal, in the midline, to the most distant point on the occiput, in the midline.
2. The greatest breadth of the cranium perpendicular to the median sagittal plane, and avoiding the supramastoid crests.
3. Cranial height measured from basion (midpoint on the anterior border of the foramen magnum) to bregma (intersection of the coronal and sagittal sutures).
4. From basion (see *3*) to nasion (midpoint of the naso-frontal suture).
5. Maximum width between the lateral surfaces of the zygomatic arches measured perpendicular to the median sagittal plane.
6. From basion (see *3*) to the most anterior point on the maxilla in the median sagittal plane.
7. Lowest point on the alveolar border between the central incisors to nasion (see *4*).
8. Maximum breadth of the palate taken on the outside of the alveolar borders.
9. The length of the mastoid measured perpendicular to the plane determined by the lower borders of the orbits and the upper borders of the auditory meatuses (= Frankfort plane). The upper arm of the sliding calipers is aligned with the upper border of the auditory meatus, and the distance (perpendicular to the Frankfort plane) to the tip of the mastoid is measured.
10. Height from the lowest median point on the jaw (menton) to the lower alveolar point (bony process between the central incisors). If the menton is in a notch, then the measurement is taken from a line tangent to the lowest points on the margins lateral to the notch.
11. Mandibular body height as measured between the first and second molars.
12. From the most anterior point on the mandibular symphysis to an imaginary point formed by the posterior margin of the ramus and the antero-posterior axis of the body, and measured parallel to the axis.
13. The thickness of the mandibular body measured at the level of the second molar parallel to the vertical axis of the body.
14. The smallest antero-posterior diameter of the ramus of the jaw.
15. The distance between the most anterior point on the mandibular ramus and the line connecting the most posterior point on the condyle and the angle of the jaw.
16. Height measured from the uppermost point on the condyle to the middle of the inferior border of the body parallel to the vertical axis of the ramus. (The middle of the ramus on the inferior margin is not a distinct point but can be easily estimated.) For Japanese mandibles, measure to gonion (see *17*).
17. Maximum diameter, externally, on the angles of the jaw (gonion).
18. Femur length taken maximally, but perpendicular to a line defined by the distal-most points of the two distal condyles (so-called oblique or standing length).
19. Greatest diameter of femur head.

20. Least transverse diameter of shaft of femur.
21. Width of the distal end of the femur (epicondylar breadth).
22. Ischial length measured from where the long axis of the ischium crosses the ischial tuberosity to a point in the acetabulum that is defined as the intersection of the long axes of the pubis and the ischium.
23. Pubic length measured from the point in the acetabulum defined in *22* to the upper extremity of the symphyseal articular facet of the pubis.
24. Height of the sciatic notch, taken as a perpendicular dropped from the point on the posterior inferior iliac spine, where the upper border of the notch meets the auricular surface, to the anterior border of the notch itself.
25. Acetabulo-sciatic breadth, taken from the median point on the anterior border of the sciatic notch (half way between the ischial spine and the apex of the notch) to the acetabular border, and perpendicular, as far as possible, to both borders.
26. Taken from the most projecting point on the pubic portion of the acetabular border perpendicular to the innominate line, and thus to the plane of the obturator foramen.
27. The distance from the anterior iliac spine to the nearest point on the auricular surface, and subtracted from the distance from the anterior iliac spine to the nearest point on the border of the sciatic notch.
28. Maximum length of the humerus.
29. Maximum epicondylar width of the humerus.
30. Maximum length of the clavicle.
31. Minimum circumference of the shaft of the humerus.
32. Maximum length of the radius.
33. Circumference of the radius at the midpoint of the shaft.
34. Circumference of the head of the radius.
35. Maximum medio-lateral breadth of the distal epiphysis of the radius.
36. Maximum length of the ulna.
37. Transverse diameter of the shaft of the ulna taken at the point of greatest development of the crista.
38. Maximum diameter of the capitulum of the ulna.
39. Maximum length of the tibia from the lateral condyle to the malleolus.
40. Maximum antero-posterior diameter of the shaft of the tibia at its midpoint.
41. Least circumference of the shaft of the tibia.
42. Maximum breadth of the proximal epiphysis of the tibia.
43. Anatomical breadth of the scapula (maximum distance between the medial and the inferior angles).
44. Anatomical length of the scapula (the distance between the center of the glenoid cavity and the point where the spine, or its projection, intersects the vertebral border).
45. Projective length of the spine of the scapula (distance from the most projecting point on the acromion to the point where the spine, or its projection, intersects the vertebral border).
46. Length of the glenoid cavity of the scapula—from the most cephalic point to the most caudal.
47. Breadth of the glenoid cavity of the scapula taken perpendicular to *46*.
48. Ischium-pubis index formed by dividing the pubic length, measured from the upper end of the pubic symphysis to the nearest point on the border of the acetabulum, by the ischium length, measured from the point where the axis of the ischium crosses the ischial tuberosity to the most distant point on the border of the acetabulum.
49. Total breadth of the atlas measured between the apexes of the transverse processes.

Multivariate Analysis for the Identification of Race from Crania

W. W. Howells

Dr. Giles' paper makes clear the nature and application of the statistical procedure referred to as a discriminant function, so that I can omit a description here. Dr. Giles discusses the function's application in the determination of the sex of a skeleton. He has also (Giles and Elliot, 1962) applied the method of the determination of race when the possibilities are White, Negro, and American Indian. Here I shall present another exploration of the possibilities of the method; i.e., when the attempt is to distinguish between the skulls of U.S. Whites and U.S. Negroes, which could be a useful element in identification in the case of an individual or mass disasters.

To begin with, we must recognize certain special aspects of the U.S. "Negro" population. Our "White" population is essentially of European origin, and the basis of our "Black" population is of course African. There has been considerable inter-breeding between the two during their 400 years in America, the issue of which is biologically hybrid but socially Negro. That is to say, the flow of genes has been to all intents and purposes one way: into the "Black" population, the much slighter, opposite flow coming from a small number of individuals whose ancestry is so pre-ponderantly European as to enable them to "pass for White," and become so socially. The addition of White genes to the immigrant African pool has been estimated several times—there is no precise evidence—as of the order of 30%. This, of course, does not mean that every "Black" is 30% "White," but rather that this is the ancestry character of the Negro gene pool as a whole. Individual U.S. Negroes range from "pass-for-Whites" to those who may still be completely African genealogically. Thus, the social point of division is different from the biological division point, if such could be thought of, which would be in the middle range of the gene balance from the two ancestral sides.

A discriminant function is blind to such niceties: reviewing purely biological evidence, like a skull, it cannot return a social answer, such as identifying as "Black" a skull whose owner may in fact have been biologically more European than African. A discriminant can give an answer only when it knows the question, and it would be extremely difficult to find material to frame the question implied by the social distinctions I have discussed. The question asked in the analysis I am about to describe is this: can a discriminant efficiently distinguish between skulls from Europe and from Negro Africa? And will this help significantly in the correct identification of other Whites and Blacks, even when the latter are members of the U.S. Negro population as I have specified it?

The material used in this study is approximately 100 skulls of each sex and each race, or continental group, taken from a much larger multiracial study I have under way (Howells, in press). To represent Europeans, I have here merged two populations: Norwegians of medieval Oslo, and more recent Austrians from a small village, Berg, in Carinthia. These two differ somewhat in character, ranging from long-headed to round-headed among other things but, by joining them in about equal numbers, I have 111 males and 98 females to make a sort of generalized White group. For the Africans I have joined Dogons, from Mali in West Africa, and Zulus from South Africa. Thus, black Africa is also represented by a somewhat generalized, but not too heterogeneous, group divided into 103 males and 99 females. One difficulty is that the true sex is known only for the Zulu, the other groups having, of necessity, been sexed by eyeball, and with the attendant uncertainty described by Dr. Giles. Definite knowledge of sex is, of course, required in his study; what is essential here is definite knowledge of race, and that we have.

For each specimen, 70 measurements, or angles, are available. All can be, and have been, used together in a discriminant function. But to get a function that is of a size for more practical applications, I have used a preliminary computer program, which simplifies computation and improves results; and I have also selected a much smaller combination of measurements that is just as apt to do the discrimination as efficiently as possible, in fact probably even more efficiently than the whole set of 70 taken at once.

For males, the function arrived at is shown in Table LVI. The figures are the discriminant weights, to be multiplied with the raw measurements of an individual, in millimeters or degrees, and the sum of the products is the discriminant score. These weights are the $b_1, b_2 \ldots b_n$ coefficients in Dr. Giles' paper. The measurements are defined in the Appendix (page 119).

TABLE LVI—Male Discriminant Function Weights

1	Basion-bregma skull height	+ 0.1068
3	Biauricular skull base breadth	− 0.2347
4	Biasterionic occipital breadth	− 0.2214
5	Basion-prosthion face length	+ 0.1161
6	Nasal breadth	+ 0.4640
9	Bifrontal breadth	+ 0.2522
14	Cheekbone height	− 0.2532
15	Supraorbital projection	− 0.3889
17	Nasion-subtense fraction	− 0.1647
18	Bregma-subtense fraction	+ 0.0778
20	Subspinale radius	− 0.3594
21	Prosthion radius	+ 0.3927
22	Zygoorbitale radius	− 0.1703
26	Naso-dacryal angle	+ 0.0496
29	Parietal angle	+ 0.1699

Figure 25 shows how the discriminant scores of the individuals are distributed. The European Whites and African Blacks, from whom the function was computed, are discriminated 100%, with room to spare, and with the dividing line at about 19.0 on the scale. Now, discrimination is bound to be better for the series on which it is based than for others not so involved. That is because the discrimination, in such a case, has two components. One is the general morphological difference between Europeans and Africans that we are attempting to analyze and use. The other component is a discrimination that is specific to the samples concerned. The discriminant function is a powerful tool with no mind of its own. It knows only that it is being asked to differentiate two groups of individuals, nothing more. Now it would furnish *some* degree of discrimination between two samples that were actually drawn from the same population, because there would exist chance sample differences, which have nothing to do with racial morphology, but which are specific to the particular groups of skulls used. One could, after all, by two or three measurements, readily distinguish between two brothers. At any rate, this component of specific, or sampling, discrimination will spuriously increase the differentiation of the groups, if what is wanted is a distinction based only on the racial component.

This element is, I am sure, not great in the present instance, but it must be borne in mind. The first test of the function is seen in the distribution on the next line, below the Whites and Blacks. This Zalavár population is European, from early medieval Hungary, and it antedates the arrival of the Hungarian (Magyar) invaders themselves. This population is from the cemeteries of a castle that was controlled then by the bishop of Salzburg, and it apparently was composed of a potpourri of Frankish, German, and Slavic elements. It is not really physically as heterogeneous as this sounds, and is in fact rather close morphologically to the Norwegians included in the main White sample.

The distribution shown is that of the discriminant scores, computed on the White-Black function, of 55 skulls judged by me to be male. It is seen to be shifted somewhat in a plus direction relative to the basic White sample. This I take to result, at least in part, from the effect I have just described, a "spurious" element having augmented the discrimination of the original populations, which might otherwise also be closer together. The Zalavár distribution, however, seems normal, and it lies entirely in the White range, with the exception of a single individual who is just over the border in the Black part of the scale, though not as far as any of the actual Blacks.

This test group firmly supports the efficiency and validity of the function, especially with the qualification that other Black and White *test* groups (as opposed to the original ones) may also be expected to lie nearer the center. The second test group is 34 supposedly male skulls of the Teita, a Bantu-speaking tribe of Kenya. Their score distribution, in Figure 25, transgresses the White-Black boundary to a greater extent than does that of the Zalavár series, with a quarter (eight individuals) being classed as White. Now the idea has frequently been expressed that some East Africans have a significant prehistoric "White" element in their genetic makeup, causing them to differ varyingly from the basic Negro population of sub-Saharan Africa. This may be supported by the appearance of certain East African peoples, but I know of no reason to credit the Teita with such an element, and much other evidence, which I shall not cite, makes their skulls seem basically like those of the Dogon and Zulu. There remains the possibility of some such "White" effect, but it is safer to assume that the discriminant function does not assign the Teita very efficiently.

The next group, shown on the fourth line, consists of the only other male skulls from West or Central Africa that I have so far measured. They number only six, comprising three Dahomeans and three Pygmies. In spite of the small number, their decidedly Black position on the scale suggests that the function does indeed give a

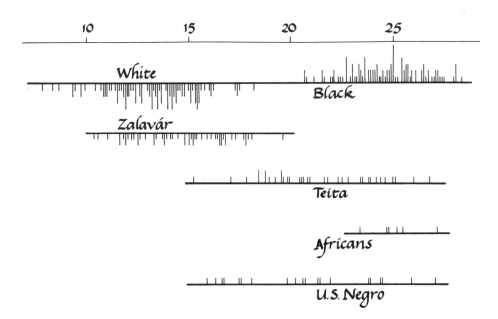

Figure 25. Distribution of scores on the male discriminant function.

good diagnosis of Black African skull form, and that the Teita, as we have seen, may be less representative of other Africans.

The proof of the pudding is in the last group, that of actual U.S. Negro skulls. These form part of the Terry Collection, from dissecting-room cadavers at Washington University in St. Louis, and now in the National Museum of Natural History in Washington. They are, of course, known as to identity, age, sex, and race, though information as to race, beyond a mere record of White or Negro, is rather unsatisfactory, and I cannot say what range of White admixture may be represented in this sample. I assume it is not untypical.

Through the kindness of Drs. Stewart and Angel, I measured 20 males for the purpose of this seminar. Their scores, as shown in Figure 25, correspond in range with those of the East African Teita, though a somewhat larger proportion, seven individuals out of 20, lies on the White side of the dividing line. They are all, however, at the upper end of the White zone, so that the distribution is consistent with the actual situation of the Negro population. This is, as I said earlier, that of a population drawn from an African region of unknown extent, whose morphological and genetic variation has been further stretched out by the reception of White admixture, which has by no means become distributed evenly in that population through panmixia. Whether the position of those individuals in the upper part of the White zone could possibly be read in gross terms of fractions of White ancestry, I cannot say.

This function is not a perfect solution of the identification problem posed here, since it does not isolate U.S. Negroes from Whites. I have explained the principal reason, that the U.S. Negro population is far from being fully "African," and that it contains individuals more White than Black. The function is probably a relatively efficient one, but more work could be done along these lines, including the analysis of bones of the skeleton. Yet even this function may be quite useful as it stands. In the results, no U.S. Negro (the sample is of course very small) has a score below 16, and only one White skull out of 166 (including the Zalavár series) has a score above 18. Allowing that the first figure might be lowered somewhat, we might conclude that any score below 16 almost certainly identifies a White skull, and any above 18 almost certainly a Black. This division point could correctly assign a very large proportion of actual Whites, and thus a great majority of possible disaster victims, as well as about 70% of U.S. Negroes, while leaving the rest to be identified by any other possible means.

Table LVII gives a discriminant function, also using 15 measurements, for female skulls. The discrimination of the original groups (in Figure 26) is less perfect than in the males. One Black skull is misclassed as White, by the barest of margins, and in general, the two distributions approach one another more closely, with a division

TABLE LVII—Female Discriminant Function Weights

1	Basion-bregma skull height	+ 0.1327
3	Biauricular skull base breadth	− 0.2369
6	Nasal breadth	+ 0.4174
8	Mastoid length	+ 0.1381
11	Naso-dacryal subtense	− 0.1581
12	Simotic subtense	− 0.5424
13	Malar subtense	+ 0.2400
14	Cheekbone height	− 0.1557
16	Glabella projection	− 0.4398
19	Nasion radius	+ 0.1828
23	Zygomaxillare radius	− 0.2320
24	Nasion angle	+ 0.2055
25	Zygomaxillary angle	+ 0.0655
27	Simotic angle	+ 0.0036
28	Frontal angle	− 0.0693

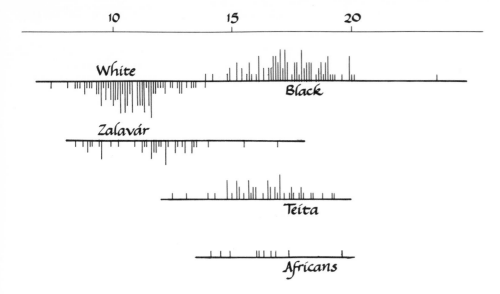

Figure 26. Distribution of scores on the female discriminant function.

point at about 13.93. If the function is less efficient, sex may be involved. It is a fact that some of the measurement differences between the races, including biauricular breadth, nasal breadth, and cheekbone height, all of which are important, are greater in the males, both absolutely and as rated by the analysis of variance.

Test groups, however, support the general efficiency of the discriminant, with Zalavár (European) and Teita (African) again being closer to the center of the range in their main distributions. Three Zalavár* individuals are misclassed as Black, but only three Teita females are misclassed as White, a smaller number than in the males, out of a substantially larger total (49 skulls). Ten other Africans that were judged female make up a mixed bag consisting of still another Teita, three Haya (another Kenya tribe), three Dahomeans, two Pygmies, and one Cape Coloured. All are classed as Black by the discriminant. Thus, the function distinguishes between Europeans and sub-Saharan Africans in a very high proportion of the cases. Unfortunately, I have not had time to test a sample of U.S. Negro females. I can only assume that the results would be like those for males, namely a distribution that carries over into the upper part of the White range. That is, about one third would be misclassified on an absolute division and, at best, part of the White range might be marked off as a zone into which some U.S. Negroes would fall.

On the whole, the results in both males and females are very good. The discriminants distinguish race (when this is African versus European, excluding hybrids) better than they can sex. This is the more impressive, since I doubt that my colleagues feel that racial distinctions can be made by eye with such a degree of confidence and reliability.

Dr. Giles notes that it is decidely helpful to know the race of a skull when applying a discriminant for sex. Since the discriminants found above differ noticeably, it is probably important to know the sex of a skull when applying a discriminant for race. One way to obviate decisions as to sex, however, is to apply simultaneous multiple discriminants, those which attempt to assign any individual, not to one of two groups only, but to one of several; in this case White male, Black male, White female, and Black female. Multiple discriminants are described by Cooley and Lohnes (1962). They consist of coordinate axes, which are used simultaneously at right angles, to

---

*In my original data records, I find a note that one of these women, the individual at the very top of the range, with a score of 16.9, was "peculiarly Negroid-looking." The score may only reflect this unusual appearance, but it is within the realm of possibility that an African was in fact present in this somewhat cosmopolitan community.

plot individuals in more than one dimension, and the maximum number of such functions is one less than the number of groups involved.

By using 16 measurements, such a set has been found here, for the four groups named above. Three functions are possible, but the last is quite insignificant (it contributes only 0.60% of the total discrimination possible) and may be ignored as meaningless. Thus, two functions are shown in Table LVIII that yield pairs of scores for all individuals, and these scores allow them to be plotted in two dimensions as in Figure 27. (In the figure, all the scores have been standardized—i.e., the main axes are the averages for all group score means, and the scores have been divided by standard deviations to make a group distribution approximately circular.)

TABLE LVIII—Race/Sex Multiple Discriminant Weights

		Function 1	Function 2
1	Basion-bregma skull height	− 0.1069	+ 0.0933
2	Bizygomatic breadth	+ 0.0666	+ 0.4979
3	Biauricular skull base breadth	+ 0.2538	− 0.2813
4	Biasterionic occipital breadth	+ 0.1520	− 0.0318
6	Nasal breadth	− 0.4357	+ 0.1048
7	Palate breadth	− 0.1315	+ 0.1667
8	Mastoid length	− 0.0610	+ 0.2267
9	Bifrontal breadth	− 0.2353	+ 0.0139
10	Dacryon subtense	+ 0.2433	− 0.0606
11	Naso-dacryal subtense	+ 0.4729	− 0.1279
14	Cheekbone height	+ 0.2388	− 0.0893
15	Supraorbital projection	+ 0.2288	+ 0.3959
16	Glabella projection	+ 0.4541	+ 0.6141
18	Bregma-subtense fraction	− 0.0587	+ 0.0883
24	Nasion angle	− 0.1056	− 0.0372
29	Parietal angle	− 0.1319	+ 0.0434

It may be said at once that Function 1 strongly tends to be simply a race discriminator, and Function 2, less specifically, a sex discriminator, though neither has completely the character described (see below). Since they contribute 78.85% and 20.55%, respectively, to the total possible discrimination, the diversity among the four groups is greater in race than in sex, and this leads to greater possible discrimination for race, which is once again demonstrated.

In addition to the general impression of discrimination furnished by the graph, the predicted affiliation of an individual can be precisely computed. This computation is more complex than for a single discriminant, but it is simple with a computer, which would be well worth its application in the case of important problems or mass disasters.

The following is the primary result from assigning the individuals of the original groups in a "hits/misses" tabulation:

Actual Placement	Predicted Placement			
	White male	Black male	White female	Black female
White male	100	1	10	0
Black male	0	92	0	11
White female	7	1	100	0
Black female	0	13	0	86

This tabulation relates predicted (columns) to actual (rows) placement; e.g., in the first *row*, all skulls are White male, of which one is classed as Black male and ten as White female. Virtually 90% (89.79%) of all the cases fall in the correct race and sex; 43 out of 421 are misclassed, but the errors are almost all as to sex,

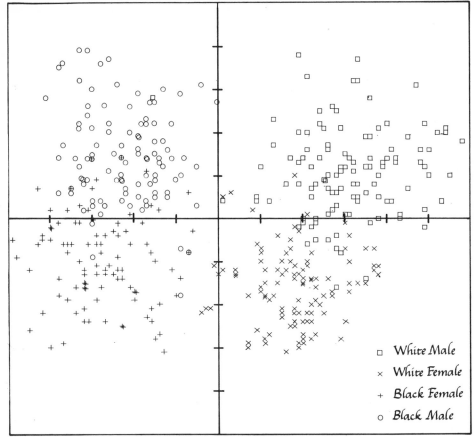

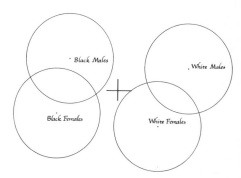

Figure 28. Means and 95% probability circles of four groups on two functions. Compare with Figure 27.

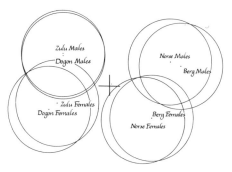

Figure 29. Means and 95% probability circles of eight original populations used for Whites and Blacks. Compare with Figure 27.

□ White Male
× White Female
+ Black Female
○ Black Male

Figure 27. Distributions of scores of individual White and Black males and females on two functions in four-group analysis.

not race. Only one White male and one White female are miscast, both as Black male; no Blacks are classed as White at all.

This also accords closely with previous results: a very high reliability for race, but with misclassing for sex amounting to nearly 10%. Thus, a result is arrived at in which assignment by sex is no worse than by other methods, while assignment by race is correct for 419 out of 421 cases (in these samples). Of course, correct sex here means agreement with visual assessment, not known sex, true sex being recorded only for the Zulus.

Another application to the test groups also gives quite good results, which are simply listed herewith as to their resulting errors.

Zalavár male:	2/54 classed as Black (no errors of sex)
Zalavár female:	3/45 classed as Black (9 errors of sex)
Teita male:	9/34 classed as White (5 errors of sex)
Teita female:	2/49 classed as White (4 errors of sex)
African male:	0/6 classed as White (no errors of sex)
African female:	0/10 classed as White (2 errors of sex)
U.S. Negro male:	8/20 classed as White (2 errors of sex, both among the "Whites")

At the cost of greater labor, but without requiring a knowledge of sex, these answers overall are just about as good as those for the separate male and female functions.

The first function does not actually constitute a racial discriminator entirely by itself, although there is not much overlap along the first axis. Figure 28 shows the same field as Figure 27, but it plots only the mean point of each of the race/sex groups, which are enclosed by a circle with a radius of two standard deviations which in turn, is expected to encompass just over 95% of cases in the normal distribution. From this it may be seen that the line of best discrimination for race is not the same as the vertical axis, but is slightly oblique to it. Thus, both functions contribute to racial discrimination.

As a minor point, it may be noted that the actual distributions in Figure 27 do not seem to approach the circle already referred to, as they should from the standardization applied to them. This is because the component series for both Whites and Blacks differ somewhat in their positions on the functions. This is shown in Figure 29, in which the mean points for each subgroup appears, and where, as before, they are surrounded by circles of the same diameter. For example, the two circles for the Norse and Berg White females, when taken together, correspond better to the somewhat elliptical scatter of the White female individuals seen in Figure 27.

This research, of which the present study forms a part, was supported by Grant Number GS–664 from the National Science Foundation. The graphs were drawn by Miss Susan Davis. Computation was done at the Harvard Computing Center, and such work was aided by funds from the Department of Anthropology. The programs for discrimination and classification are contained in K. Jones' Multiple Statistical Analyzer series of programs (Jones, 1964). The program to select a reduced set of measurements was written for me several years ago by Dr. Roger Carlson of the University of Missouri.

Literature Cited

Cooley, W. W., and Lohnes, P. R.
  1962. *Multivariate Procedures for the Behavioral Sciences.* New York: Wiley. 211 pages.
Giles, E., and Elliot, O.
  1962. Race Identification from Cranial Measurements. *Journal of Forensic Sciences,* 7:147-157.
Howells, W. W.
  [In press.] *Cranial Variation in Man.*
Jones, K. J.
  1964. *The Multivariate Statistical Analyzer.* A system of FORTRAN II programs to be run under 7090-4 FORTRAN monitor system. Harvard Cooperative Society. 179 pages.

APPENDIX

Practical Application

This paper was primarily intended to illustrate a method. It has been based on a larger study, and this calls for some remarks. Other formulae, using other measurements, could be computed from the same material, and this would allow for work with an incomplete skull, using what measurements were possible in such a case. On the other hand, the larger study referred to used some measurements which vary from, or are additional to, those in standard textbooks. For this reason, the measurements and the instruments needed to take them are specifically described below.

To use the basic formulae in the article, the procedure would be like that in Giles' article, especially if one wanted to avoid the more complex computations. First estimate the sex, perhaps by using Giles' functions. Then take each of the measurements listed in the appropriate function. Multiply each by the corresponding value in the function, as listed, and give the product the plus or minus sign shown. Sum all these to produce the discriminant score. If the value is above 19.0 for a male, or 13.93 for a female, assume the subject is Negro. If below, the subject is probably White but because of mixture remember that there also is a decreasing probability of Negro, which would be negligible below 16.0 for males and 12.0 for females. (The last figure is an estimate, since no U.S. Negro females were measured. There are, of course, no absolute values to fall back on—see Giles' remarks on probabilities and populations.)

Instruments

Spreading calipers. Standard; e.g., Siber Hegner, New York.

Sliding calipers. Standard; e.g., Siber Hegner; or dial reading, e.g., Helios (which can be supplied with needle points), from Karl Neise, New York.

Coordinate caliper. Standard; e.g., Siber Hegner, listed as #12.

Radiometer. Larger coordinate caliper; e.g., Siber Hegner #13 (Aichel caliper), fitted with rounded points for insertion in ear openings.

Simometer. Coordinate caliper with angled points, but which can be brought to a common point for small measurements such as nasal bones. Not supplied by instrument makers; it must be made specially.

Palatometer. Small coordinate caliper; e.g., Siber Hegner #31.

Definitions of Cranial Measurements*

All measurements are taken in millimeters except #12, simotic subtense, which is in tenths of a millimeter. Angles are expressed in degrees. Instruments are the spreading caliper, sliding caliper, coordinate caliper (for measuring a perpendicular or subtense to a line or chord), and radiometer (which has plugs to fit the ear openings and so measures distances, or radii, from this transmeatal axis). Fuller descriptions of technique are given in Howells (in press).

---

*For definitions of landmarks referred to, see page 121.

1. Basion-bregma skull height: distance from bregma to basion. Spreading caliper.
2. Bizygomatic breadth: the maximum breadth across the zygomatic arches, wherever found, but perpendicular to the median plane. Sliding caliper.
3. Biauricular skull base breadth: the least exterior breadth across the roots of the zygomatic processes, wherever found. Sliding caliper.
4. Biasterionic occipital breadth: direct measurement from one asterion to the other. Sliding caliper.
5. Basion-prosthion face length: the facial length from prosthion to basion. Sliding caliper.
6. Nasal breadth: the distance between the anterior edges of the nasal aperture at its widest extent. Sliding caliper.
7. Palate breadth, external: the greatest breadth across the alveolar borders wherever found, but perpendicular to the median plane. Sliding caliper.
8. Mastoid length: the length of the mastoid process below, and perpendicular to, the eye-ear plane, in the vertical plane. Sliding caliper.
9. Bifrontal breadth: the breadth across the frontal bone between frontomalare anterior on each side; i.e., the most anterior point on the frontomalar suture. Sliding or coordinate caliper.
10. Dacryon subtense: the mean subtense from dacryon (average of two sides) to the biorbital breadth, measured between the anterior surfaces of the lateral orbital borders. Coordinate caliper.
11. Naso-dacryal subtense: the subtense from the deepest point in the profile of the nasal bones to the interorbital breadth between the dacrya. Simometer.
12. Simotic subtense: the subtense from the nasal bridge to the least breadth of the nasal bones. Simometer.
13. Malar subtense: the maximum subtense from the convexity of the malar angle to the maximum length of the bone, at the level of the zygomaticofacial foramen, on the left side. Coordinate caliper.
14. Cheekbone height: the minimum distance, in any direction, from the lower border of the orbit to the lower margin of the maxilla, mesial to the masseter attachment, on the left side. Sliding caliper.
15. Supraorbital projection: the maximum projection of the left supraorbital arch between the midline, in the region of glabella or above, and the frontal bone just anterior to the temporal line in its forward part, and measured as a subtense to the line defined. Coordinate caliper.
16. Glabella projection: the maximum projection of the midline profile between nasion and supraglabellare (or the point at which the convex profile of the frontal bone changes to join the prominence of the glabellar region), measured as a subtense. Palatometer.
17. Nasion-subtense fraction: the distance along the nasion-bregma chord, recorded from nasion, at which the maximum subtense to that chord is found. Coordinate caliper.
18. Bregma-subtense fraction: the distance along the bregma-lambda chord, recorded from bregma, at which the maximum subtense to that chord is found. Coordinate caliper.
19. Nasion radius: the perpendicular to the transmeatal axis from nasion. Radiometer.
20. Subspinale radius: the perpendicular to the transmeatal axis from subspinale. Radiometer.
21. Prosthion radius: the perpendicular to the transmeatal axis from prosthion. Radiometer.
22. Zygoorbitale radius: the perpendicular to the transmeatal axis from the left zygoorbitale. Radiometer.
23. Zygomaxillare radius: the perpendicular to the transmeatal axis from the left zygomaxillare anterior. Radiometer.

NOTE: the following are angles, which may be either drawn or computed from the appropriate measurements.

24. Nasion angle (basion-prosthion): of the facial triangle, the angle at nasion, whose sides are basion-nasion and nasion-prosthion. (This requires the measurement of basion-prosthion, #5; also basion-nasion and nasion-prosthion lengths.)
25. Zygomaxillare angle: the angle at subspinale whose two sides reach from this point to zygomaxillare anterior, left and right. (This requires the measurement of the bimaxillary chord and zygomaxillary subtense from the subspinale thereto.) Coordinate caliper.
26. Naso-dacryal angle: the angle formed at the midline of the nasal bones, whose sides reach from this point to dacryon, left and right. (This requires naso-dacryal subtense, #11, and interorbital breadth, from dacryon to dacryon.) Simometer.
27. Simotic angle: the angle at the midline of the nasal bones, at their narrowest point, whose sides reach to the end points of the minimum breadth of the nasal bones. (This requires simotic subtense, #12, and least nasal breadth.) Simometer.
28. Frontal angle: in the sagittal plane, the angle underlying the curvature of the frontal bone at its maximum height above the frontal chord. (This requires nasion-bregma chord, nasion-bregma subtense thereto, and nasion-subtense fraction, #17.) Coordinate caliper.
29. Parietal angle: in the sagittal plane, the angle underlying the curvature of the parietal bones along the sagittal suture, and at its maximum height above the parietal chord. (This requires bregma-lambda chord, bregma-lambda subtense thereto, and bregma subtense fraction, #18.) Coordinate caliper.

Definitions of Landmarks

Asterion: the common meeting point of the temporal, parietal, and occipital bones, on either side.

Basion: on the anterior border of the foramen magnum, in the midline, at the position pointed to by the apex of the triangular surface at the base of either condyle; i.e., the average position from the crests bordering this area.

Bregma: the posterior border of the frontal bone in the median plane.

Dacryon: the apex of the lacrimal fossa, as it impinges on the frontal bone.

Frontomalare anterior: the most anterior point on the frontomalar suture. It may be found with the side of a pencil lead held in the transverse plane.

Lambda: the apex of the occipital bone at its junction with the parietals, in the midline.

Nasion: the intersection of the fronto-nasal suture and the median plane.

Prosthion: the most anteriorly prominent point, in the midline, on the alveolar border, and above the septum between the central incisors.

Subspinale: the deepest point seen in the profile below the anterior nasal spine.

Zygomaxillare anterior: the intersection of the zygomaxillary suture and the limit of the attachment of the masseter muscle, on the facial surface.

Zygoorbitale: the intersection of the orbital margin and the zygomaxillary suture.

The Role of the Forensic Pathologist in the Identification of Human Remains

Geoffrey T. Mann and Hobart R. Wood

In ordinary life, the identification of persons by sight alone leads to endless mistakes, yet without any particular inconvenience. In connection with criminal identification, however, serious results may occur.

The human eye and photography are notoriously unreliable, even in the identification of recently dead persons. Greater difficulties are encountered with mutilated, decomposed, or fragmentary remains.

In 1927, a "body," who had been identified by photograph, turned up at her own funeral protesting her interment.

In 1953, the photo of a man wanted for information in connection with a murder, was televised. Dozens of people said they had seen him—often simultaneously—hundreds of miles apart. Actually, the man was lying dead in a cellar at that time.

Early attempts to establish a reliable method of identification were made by Bertillon in 1880. The system named after him employed detailed descriptions of the features and measurements of height, sitting height, span, length of certain bones, skull measurements, etc. In police work, this has been largely replaced by fingerprinting, although outlines of the method are still used in the FBI "Wanted" sheets.

The means available to the forensic pathologist for identification are:

1. Complexion, racial color, eyes
2. Likeness of features
3. Occupation marks
4. Clothes, articles in pockets, jewelry
5. Deformities, birth marks, etc.
6. Injuries, scars, tattoos
7. Fingerprinting
8. Stature, weight
9. Sex
10. Age
11. Teeth, dentures
12. Hair

Complexion

The body should be examined in daylight. Vital shades such as pale, florid, sallow, disappear soon after death; such things as freckles and pimples last a little longer.

Bodies in water lose hair and skin. The color of the eyes changes from blue to grey to brown.

Likeness of Features

Death alters the expression very rapidly, so little reliance can be placed upon this mode of identification. In particular, decomposed bodies are distorted by gas and

123

should be looked at again, after the autopsy, when the gas has escaped and the fluids have drained, and when the original shapes are better recognizable.

If only bones are available, the facial characteristics of a skull may be reconstructed with the help of a sculptor.

Occupation Marks

Stains: Paint, dye, grease, flour, etc., may be found on the skin and clothing.

Debris under the fingernails, in the ears, or in the pockets may provide clues.

Callosities and deformities may be characteristic of certain professions. The shape and condition of the hands will usually distinguish the laborer from the professional, or unemployed man. Peeling potatoes causes superficial cuts on the fingertips; tailors may show callosities on the thumb, from holding scissors, and needlepricks on the fingertips. Playing the violin or cello also causes characteristic callosities. Metalworkers may show a siderotic skin pigmentation. Nicotine stains on the fingers and on the back of the incisor teeth mark the cigarette smoker; thick and burnt skin on the thumb, and perhaps increased wear on certain teeth, may identify a pipe-smoker.

These marks are helpful but not conclusive. Their presence is indicative of a certain job or habit; their absence does not exclude it.

Clothes, etc.

These are usually of great value: the maker's tags, laundry marks, or dyer's marks provide useful information. "Invisible" ink is commonly used to mark clothes; they should, therefore, be examined under ultraviolet light.

Watchmakers and jewelers often use private marks in their repairs.

Cigarette packages bear code symbols that indicate the date and place of manufacture.

Social security cards, driver's licenses, etc., are, of course, good circumstantial evidence by which to establish a body's identity.

Deformities, Birthmarks, etc.

Congenital dislocations, cleft palates, harelips, moles, or port-wine stains are of great value and should be carefully noted.

Injuries, Scars, Tattoos

Old fractures, accidental or operative scars, marks from boils, etc., should be noted, described, and measured.

If X-rays of the living person are available, the presence of arthritic and degenerative changes of the large joints and the spine are important features to note and compare.

Tattoos may occur anywhere on the body. Names, dates, symbols of occupation or trade (sailors, soldiers) all furnish useful information. They also give an idea in what sort of circles the deceased moved (obscene ornaments, etc.). The marks may become obscured in decomposed bodies, but they reappear if the superficial dermis is stripped.

In 1935, James Smith disappeared from Sydney, Australia. Two weeks later a shark was caught on the beach and sold to an aquarium. There it vomited a human arm which showed tattoo marks that were identified as Smith's.

Fingerprinting

This is undoubtedly the safest and most accurate means of identification. In A.D. 782, the Chinese used fingerprints as substitutes for signatures. In 1853, Sir William Herschel, a civil servant in India, used this method to prevent Indian pensioners from collecting their pensions more than once.

Fingerprinting's use in criminology was gradually adopted in England, and later in France and Germany, where the Bertillon system was put into general use.

At the time of birth, a fine pattern of ridges develops in the skin on the balls of the fingers, thumbs, parts of the palms, and soles of the feet.

These ridges are arranged in:

Loops _____	67%
Whorls _____	25%
Arches _____	6-7%
Composite forms _____	1-2%

and serve for primary classification.

Finer details, e.g., branching, coalescence, etc., permit subgrouping.

Sixteen to 20 points of fine comparison are accepted as proof of identity. The chances of similar prints from different fingers are about one in 64 thousand million. Unless from the same fingers, never yet in the world's crime records have two identical prints been seen.

On decomposed, or immersed bodies, difficulties may arise; often, however, glove-like pieces of skin can be removed and may give perfect prints.

Stature and Weight

About 1.2 inches in men, and 1.5 inches in women, should be subtracted from any stature measured in footwear. Also, it should be taken into account that the corpse length is about 0.75 inch more than the living stature.

If only bones are found, their measurements can be used to reconstruct the stature by use of the tables to be found in the standard textbooks on forensic pathology and anthropology. Similarly, conclusions as to race, sex, and age can be drawn with reasonable accuracy.

Sex

Even markedly decomposed or incinerated remains may contain' tissue that is recognizable microscopically. The uterus resists decomposition longest, and sections from the pelvic region may show endometrial tissue.

In mutilated remains where the genitalia are missing, skin and mucous membranes may be used for nuclear sexing. And, of course, the well-known sex differences of the human skeleton can be used to establish the sex of bodies.

Age

In recently dead people, this seldom presents difficulties.

Wrinkles, the distribution of hair (hair in the auditory meatus rarely begins to appear before 50 years of age), the state of the teeth, etc., may all be used.

The ossification centers, the cranial sutures, and degenerative joint changes are also helpful to determine the age of skeletons.

Teeth and Dentures

In natural decomposition, teeth are practically indestructible. They are, therefore, an excellent aid in the identification of remains and in the estimation of age.

The cooperation of a dentist interested and experienced in the field of forensic dentistry is invaluable.

The following points should be noted: the number and the situation of the teeth present; the number and situation of teeth lost, including evidence of how long lost (watch for teeth lost postmortem); the arrangement, irregularities, erosion, caries, and fillings; the bridge, crown work, and dentures; and the exact shape of edentulous jaws.

The identity of a murder victim occasionally rests entirely with the dental findings. The most celebrated cases are those of Professor Webster of Harvard being convicted for the murder of Dr. Parkman, whose artificial teeth were found in a furnace, and Haigh's "acid-bath" murders in London in which the lost victim was identified by her dentist who recognized the acrylic-resin dentures.

Hair

Color, texture, dyes, etc., should be noted. Racial characteristics are less reliable than commonly believed.

Conclusion

The identification of unknown human remains is always in direct proportion to the time, care, and industry applied to the problem.

Identification of The Scars of Parturition in The Skeletal Remains of Females

T. D. Stewart

At the end of this seminar, concluding a day devoted to demonstrations of identification procedures, Dr. J. Lawrence Angel presented, and he and I commented upon, some skeletons recently processed for the FBI in the laboratory of physical anthropology of the National Museum of Natural History. Among the skeletal features pointed out by Dr. Angel, the one that seemed to arouse the most interest in the seminar audience was an alteration in the medial part of a pubic bone from an adult female that was interpreted as evidence of childbearing. Dr. Angel described the alteration as a conspicuous cavity, about the size of a small acorn, and located it dorsally, just under the midpart of the articular surface. He also pointed out that the opening of the cavity had encroached upon the dorsal margin of the articular surface, and had produced an indentation of this margin.

Rather than paraphrase Dr. Angel's explanation of how parturition produces this sort of bony scarring, I will quote from one of his publications that has appeared in the meantime (Angel, 1969, p. 432):

These [bony pelvic] changes [that result from childbirth] are consistently clearest around the pubic symphysis where pregnancy stresses the muscle and tendon attachments of the central belly wall (Rectus abdominis and both tubercle and pectineal attachments of the inguinal ligament or tendon of the Obliquus externus abdominis); where also during the birth process the arcuate and interpubic ligaments are stretched and torn and where cysts and knots of fibrocartilages follow the tears and small haemorrhages ("bruises") which occur under the ligaments, especially on the inner surface separated from the birth canal only by the bladder walls. On the anterior surface of the pubic symphysis, therefore, exostoses develop (not unlike those seen in older arthritic skeletons of either sex) and generally a spiral fossa below the pubic tubercle begins to develop even after one or two births. Posteriorly, next to lip exostoses a series of small fossae from haemorrhages and cysts after a sufficient number of births (perhaps 4–8) may coalesce into a deep groove next to the exaggerated lip at the back edge of the symphyseal face. A clear-cut development of these changes occurs after more than three births.

In this explanation, Dr. Angel has brought his anatomical knowledge to bear on:

1. Putschar's (1931) detailed analysis of a considerable amount of German autopsy material
2. My study of Eskimo pelves (Stewart, 1957), along with his own examination of these same pelves, and others from archeological sources
3. His examination of four pubic bones from U.S. females of known parity that were obtained at autopsy by Dr. J. Wallace Graham of Los Angeles.

Since adequate documentation on parity is so limited in this assemblage of material, I am sure that Dr. Angel regards his deductions as tentative, especially as regards their use in forensic interpretations. I, myself, did not go nearly this far, either in my 1957 publication, or in my brief reference to the subject in the second edition of *Gradwohl's Legal Medicine* (Stewart, 1968, pp. 142–3). The reason for this failure requires a brief historical digression.

In retrospect, I look upon the circumstances that led to my 1957 publication, which was probably the first to bring the features in question to the attention of physical anthropologists, as serendipitous in the true sense of the word; that is, they made possible, in the words of one definition, "a discovery of valuable or agreeable things not sought for." I had recently been in Japan looking at age changes in the skeletons of American soldiers killed in Korea and, in this connection, I had been giving special attention to the articular surfaces of the pubic bones (see McKern and Stewart, 1957). As a result, I had developed a concept of the normal form of the pubic symphysis without fully appreciating the fact that this concept applied to the male sex alone. With this unconscious preparation for a new experience, upon my return to Washington I undertook to study, in another connection, a collection of Eskimo skeletons. My surprise was great, therefore, when I noted among the Eskimos very differently shaped symphyses including, in some instances, depressions and/or cavities on the adjacent dorsal surfaces. Immediately, I realized that the specimens that deviated from my concept of normality were of the female sex. Thus, although I had looked at Eskimo skeletons many times before, for the first time I then was "seeing" these particular features as abnormal and limited to the female sex. The final step, of accounting for the abnormality, was easy, of course.

By having been so recently engrossed in skeletal age changes, I initially considered the parturition scars solely in terms of their effect upon the regular age-related metamorphosis of the articular surfaces. My main concern was to warn anthropologists, engaged in estimating skeletal age from the pubic symphysis, against mistaking acquired pathological changes for normal age changes. This actually is the main point of my 1957 article. That I made the same point in my chapter in the second edition of *Gradwohl's Legal Medicine* is due to the long interval between the date of revision for my chapter and the date of publication for the book. During this interval, I came to realize that the ability to interpret alterations in female pubic bones as due to parturition is, in itself, important forensically.

Greater accuracy in interpreting abnormal female pubic bones, in terms of parity, can best be achieved, of course, through the assembly and study of an adequate series of documented specimens obtained at autopsy. To this end, Dr. Angel and I appealed to the forensic pathologists present at this seminar to cooperate in this endeavor. So far, the only one who has responded is Keith Mant of London. On June 4, Dr. Mant delivered to me five pairs of beautifully prepared pubic bones of women who had borne children (seee Appendix, page 136). Unless more cooperation is forthcoming, this yield for a period of approximately six months via one man's service gives some idea of how long it will take to build up an adequate study series.*

Before Dr. Mant delivered his specimens, and thus before I had any idea as to what they would show, it had occurred to me that Dr. Angel and I might have gained a mistaken idea of the nature and frequency of pubic bone alterations in modern American females, especially from what we had seen in Eskimo skeletons. I kept wondering whether modern obstetrical procedures reduces the amount of bone scarring that apparently can occur in females living in a natural state. To check this point, I began looking at the skeletons in the Terry Collection. This collection, named for the late Robert J. Terry, a longtime professor of anatomy at Washington University, St. Louis, was derived from cadavers of Whites and American Negroes, mostly from the Greater St. Louis area, that had been assigned to the University by the State Anatomical Board between about 1914 and 1965. In 1967, the collection was deposited in the National Museum of Natural History in Washington. The documentation of the skeletons is typical of most dissecting-room populations; that

---

*By the time this report went to press, Dr. Mant had upped the number delivered to thirty. EDITOR.

is, all of the information given—sex, age, race, and cause of death—is reliable, except that for age, which in many instances is an estimate, albeit a close estimate. There is no information, unfortunately, as to whether any of the females had borne children.

The purpose of this paper, then, is to report my new observations on the differences between male and female pubic bones, with emphasis on those differences most likely attributable to trauma during parturition. These observations are offered as a supplement to Dr. Angel's oral presentation at the seminar and his subsequently published statement, quoted above in the interest of extending the basis for interpretation in forensic situations, at least until better data become available. In making the observations, I had in mind the need to know:

1. Which features occur in both sexes, either as hereditary variations or as acquired (mainly arthritic) variations?
2. What is the effect of age on the frequency and appearance of the features that occur only in females?

Considering how little is known about these important aspects of the subject, I feel justified in taking advantage of the present opportunity to expand the record of this seminar in this way.

Results

As an aid in evaluating the findings in the Terry Collection skeletons, I will first report the results of a review of the casts made in Japan from the pubic bones of American soldiers, and of a reexamination of the actual pelves of 35 female Eskimos from Point Hope, Alaska (National Museum of Natural History numbers that range from 346,004 to 346,300). The casts convinced me that I was not mistaken in remembering that the occurrence of even slight depressions, much less pits or cavities, on the dorsal surfaces adjacent to the dorsal margins of the articular surfaces is extremely rare in young adult males. Also, only occasionally does the outline of the dorsal articular margins fail to present a smooth convexity. Having a cast of only one side available, whenever I encountered one of these cases with an irregular margin I could only wish for the corresponding part on the other side so as to determine whether or not it showed a matching irregularity. Rarely, however, was an irregularity of the dorsal articular margin due to lipping, although apparently there is a gradual sharpening of the margin with age, and especially after the symphysis reaches its plateau stage.

By contrast, and again just as I remembered, the female Eskimo pubic bones include many examples with depressions, pits, and/or cavities that are located just behind the dorsal margins of the symphyseal surfaces, and (probably as a result) they are often in combination with irregularities of these margins. I judged less than half of the series (45.7%) as normal. Of the remainder, 17.2% showed depressions that ranged in size from a trace to small; 37.1% showed depressions (sometimes better described as pits or cavities), which ranged in size from medium to large. In some cases, there also was evidence of slightly more lipping of the dorsal margins, and of greater alteration of the symphyseal surfaces as a whole, than I had seen in the soldiers, but the lack of age documentation in the Eskimo females prevented interpretation.

The examination of these pelves made me realize that in the past I had looked at the pubic bones mainly in connection with determinations of sex and age. Generally, it suffices for this purpose to look only at their ventral and medial aspects. This may be one reason why illustrations of the dorsal aspect of the pubic bones are uncommon, and why the peculiar scarring that occurs here in some females was overlooked for so long. Anyway, one needs to view the bones in reverse in order to readily discover, and make the best evaluation of, the scars of parturition. It also is helpful, when looking at the posterior aspect of the pubic bones, to bring the symphyseal surfaces into natural apposition so as to be able to judge the condition of both dorsal margins at the same time. The tendency is, of course, to bring the two surfaces into actual contact, and then to conclude that the type of dorsal-margin conformation exhibited is the result of this contact. The interpubic fibrocartilage, however, is interposed between the surfaces in life and, therefore, bony contact in life is seen only rarely, and usually as a result of violent trauma.

Viewing the apposed pubic bones from different aspects also made me realize that the sequence of events in the metamorphosis of the symphyseal articular surfaces has a bearing on the appearance of the dorsal margins of these surfaces during adult life. By the beginning of the childbearing period, the dorsal margins are approaching their limit of growth, whereas the ventral margins are still far from this ultimate limit. Actually, during the 25- to 40-year age period the whole ventral half of each symphyseal surface builds up a socalled "rampart," some 4-5 mm thick. As a result, during the early part of the childbearing period the space between the two pubic bones, as viewed from above, is wide in front and narrow behind (figure 30, upper). Thereafter, this space gradually becomes narrower in front until, around age 40, when the two symphyseal surfaces reach the plateau stage, they are more or less parallel from front to back (figure 30, lower).

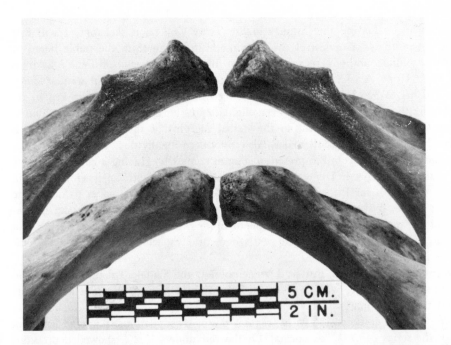

Figure 30. Superior aspect of two pairs of female pubic bones in normal apposition that demonstrate age changes in the symphysis. (Terry Collection nos. 929 and 1105, respectively.)

The earlier growth cessation on the dorsal sides of the symphyseal surfaces is, presumably, the main reason why the dorsal margins are the places where lipping tends to occur first. In this regard, the symphysis is like any other synarthrodial joint, although the amount of motion to which it is subject is quite limited. Both males and females show this lipping, and I find it difficult to say that one sex has more than the other since the maximum stage reached—usually far less than that seen in the vertebral joints—is about the same in both. On the other hand, it seems to me that the variability of the ventral margins is so great in both sexes that it is impossible to attribute any of this with certainty to parturition.

With these considerations in mind, the findings in the Terry Collection females will now be presented. I began my examination by looking at all of the younger adult females (20 to 40 years, inclusive), and which were in the most accessible part of the collection. Later, I looked at most of the older adult females (over 40 years) in the same part of the collection. The resulting sample reflects the fact that the dissecting room in St. Louis received fewer female than male cadavers; and of the females, fewer young than old individuals, fewer Whites than Negroes. This explains why I eventually viewed only 60 White females as compared with 110 Negro females, and why I failed, as will appear, to get the same distribution, by decades of age, in the two races.

Mainly, I directed my attention to the extent of scarring on the dorsal surfaces of the pubic bones near the borders of the symphyseal surfaces. Table LIX summarizes these observations. Here the size category, "trace to small," should be understood to characterize a variety of shallow depressions, usually not sharply limited and sometimes taking the form of a groove closely parallel to the articular margin. It is possible that, occasionally, what I took to be a trace of a depression or groove was an illusion created by the nature of the lipping present. Thus, if anything, this category exaggerates the amount of scarring attributable to parturition. On the other hand, I consider the category, "medium to large," to represent very definite scarring, and which range from more or less distinct depressions to unmistakable cavities. The significant thing to note, therefore, is that, according to my judgment, only about half of the female sample for each race shows any scars of this sort, and that quite likely not more than 17% show unmistakable scars. Also, there appears to be a decrease in the amount of scarring with age. This is far less evidence of parturition than I had expected to find. I was not surprised, therefore, to discover that Dr. Mant's five specimens do not show these features to a marked extent either (see Appendix, page 136).

In a number of the Terry Collection cases that exhibit "medium to large" depressions or cavities close to the dorsal margin, there is clear evidence of destruction of the adjacent part of the symphyseal surface. The result is an indentation of the dorsal margin. Figures 31-33 demonstrate this fact. Not uncommonly, on the other

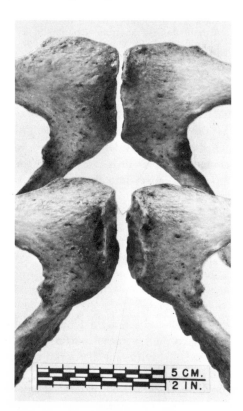 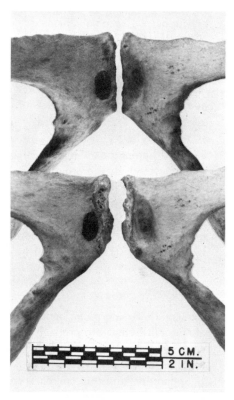 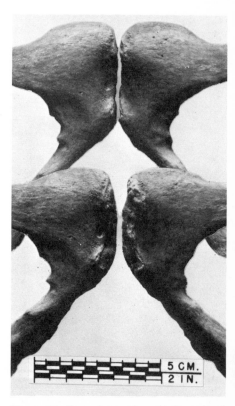

Figure 31. Two views of a single pair of female pubic bones (White, age 57) to demonstrate the extent of parturition scars. *Upper,* normal orientation; *lower,* symphysis opened normally. (Terry Collection no. 736).

Figure 32. Two views of a single pair of female pubic bones (Negro, age 35) to demonstrate the extent of parturition scars. Orientation as in Figure 31. (Terry Collection no. 766).

Figure 33. Two views of a single pair of female pubic bones (Negro, age 49) to demonstrate the extent of parturition scars. Orientation as in Figure 31. (Terry Collection no 1124R).

131

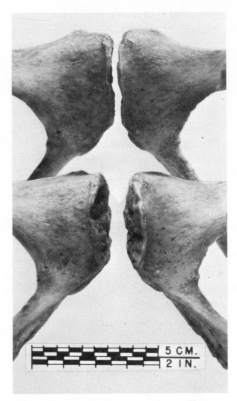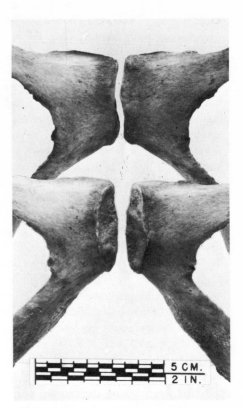

Figure 34. Two views of a single pair of female pubic bones (Negro, age 38) to show the irregularity of the dorsal margin without definite scarring. Orientation as in Figure 31. (Terry Collection no. 695R).

Figure 35. Two views of a single pair of female pubic bones (Negro, age 50) to show the irregularity of the dorsal margin without definite scarring. Orientation as in Figure 31. (Terry Collection no. 1129).

hand, female symphyses were seen in which there are irregularities of the dorsal margin without clear evidence of associated cavities (figures 34-35). Dr. Mant's cases numbers 4 and 5 are clearly in this category. In all such cases an indentation of the margin on one side is usually matched by an extrusion (sometimes with localized lipping) on the other, much as occurs when a tooth is lost and the corresponding tooth in the other jaw, lacking opposition, moves into the gap. This suggests that parturition can also affect the symphyseal surfaces directly or, alternately, that the bone here can be gradually remodeled to remove the evidence of the former presence of undermining depressions or cavities. In any case, although I gained the impression that this feature is more common in females than in males, further study is needed to determine in what ways it is really distinctive of females.

Conclusions

Unlike adult male pubic bones, those of adult females sometimes exhibit distinctive abnormalities that are probably scars attributable to the trauma of parturition. The clearest of these abnormalities are depressions and/or cavities on the dorsal surfaces adjacent to the symphyseal articular surfaces. A large cavity, it would seem, tends to undermine, and thus encroach on, the articular surface, thereby causing the dorsal margin of this surface to become irregular in outline. In addition, the appearance of the marginal irregularities in older individuals suggests that, in the course of time, bone remodeling eliminates much of the evidence of former cavities.

The symphyseal articular surfaces undergo a more or less regular metamorphosis that is both age related and most evident ventrally. For this reason, it is not as easy

TABLE LIX

Frequency of Scars of Two Sizes on the Dorsal Side of the Pubic Symphysis in 170 White and Negro Female Skeletons in the Terry Collection. Arranged by Decade of Life.

Decade of life	No.	Absent %	Trace to small %	Medium to large %
Whites				
20-29	1	—	1.7	—
30-39	7	5.0	1.7	5.0
40-49	4	—	1.7	5.0
50-59	7	8.3	1.7	1.7
60-69	15	11.7	11.6	1.7
70-79	15	16.7	8.3	—
80-89	11	8.3	6.6	3.3
Total	60	50.0	33.3	16.7
Negroes				
20-29	22	12.7	6.4	0.9
30-39	24	9.1	6.4	6.4
40-49	22	8.2	8.2	3.6
50-59	10	7.3	1.8	—
60-69	12	6.4	3.6	0.9
70-79	10	5.4	3.6	—
80-89	6	0.9	2.7	1.8
90-99	3	0.9	0.9	0.9
100-109	1	—	—	0.9
Total	110	50.9	33.6	15.4

to distinguish abnormal from normal changes on the ventral side of the symphysis, and no attempt to do so was made in the present study. Also, the limited stress to which the joint is normally subject produces lipping of the dorsal margins to about the same degree in both sexes. On the other hand, localized, extra lipping seems to develop sometimes in connection with the scars of parturition.

Modern White and Negro females, as represented in the Terry Collection skeletons, show fewer scars of parturition than do Eskimo females, as represented by a small collection of skeletons from Alaska in the National Museum of Natural History— and this in spite of (or because of?) the fact that the Eskimo females had a much shorter life expectancy. It is not possible to say that the 50% of the modern female sample which shows no scars were all nulliparas, but it is unlikely that they were, especially in view of the fact that the five cases with obstetrical histories supplied by Dr. Mant (see Appendix, page 136), as well as the four other cases obtained by Dr. Graham (Angel, 1969, Plate 2), show that some women can bear children with a minimum of scarring, or even without any scarring.

Until better material becomes available and is given more thorough study, it seems best, from the forensic standpoint, to use extreme care in interpreting the evidence in the case of an unknown adult female. At present only the major scars—medium to large dorsal cavities with or without obvious distortion of the dorsal articular margin—seem clearly indicative of parturition. Probably it will never be possible to associate accurately the degree of scarring with the true number of complete pregnancies.

Literature Cited

Angel, J. Lawrence
  1969. The Bases of Paleodemography. *American Journal of Physical Anthropology,* 30:427-37.
McKern, Thomas W., and Stewart, T. D.
  1957. Skeletal Age Changes in Young American Males, Analysed from the Standpoint of Age Identification. *Technical Report EP-45,* Environmental Protection Research

Division, Quartermaster Research and Development Center, U.S. Army, Natick, Mass.

Putschar, Walter
1931. *Entwicklung, Wachstum und Pathologie der Beckenverbindungen des Menschen, mit besonderer Berücksichtigung von Schwangershaft, Geburt und ihren Folgen.* Gustav Fischer, Jena.

Stewart. T. D.
1957. Distortion of the Pubic Symphyseal Surface in Females and its Effect on Age Determination. *American Journal of Physical Anthropology,* 15:9-18.

————

1968. Identification by the Skeletal Structures. Chapter 11 (pages 123-54) in *Gradwohl's Legal Medicine,* edited by Francis E. Camps. 2d edition, John Wright & Sons Ltd., Bristol, England.

APPENDIX

Data on five pairs of pubic bones obtained at autopsy from White females by Dr. Keith Mant of the Department of Forensic Medicine, Guy's Hospital, London, during the first half of 1969:*

Case no.	Initials	Age	No. of children	X-ray available	Photographs available
1	Y.P.	25	3	Yes	Plate 36
4	M.S.	36	2	Yes	Plate 37
5	P.S.	40	3	No	Plate 38
7	P.M.	30	2	Yes	Plate 39
8	A.O.	40	2	Yes	Plate 40

* Five other pairs supplied by Dr. Mant are from nulliparas and, therefore, are not included. I am grateful to Dr. Mant for all this material and for his enthusiastic cooperation.

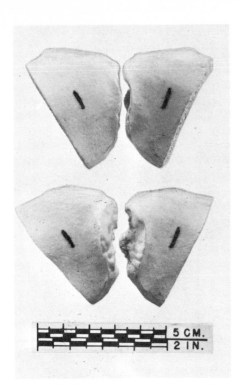

Figure 36. Two views of a single pair of female pubic bones (age 25, 3 children) to show the irregularity of the dorsal margin without definite scarring. Orientation as in Figure 31. (Mant case no. 1).

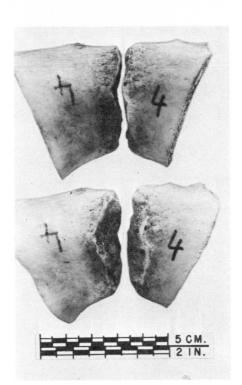

Figure 37. Two views of a single pair of female pubic bones (age 36, 2 children) to show the irregularity of the dorsal margin without definite scarring. Orientation as in Figure 31. (Mant case no. 4).

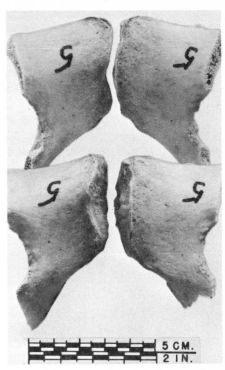

Figure 38. Two views of a single pair of female pubic bones (age 40, 3 children) to show the irregularity of the dorsal margin without definite scarring. Orientation as in Figure 31. (Mant case no. 5).

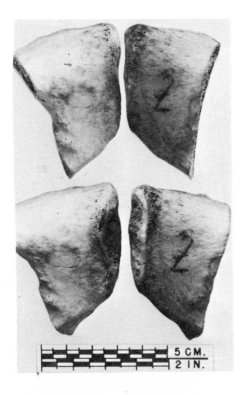

(far left)

Figure 39. Two views of a single pair of female pubic bones (age 30, 2 children) to show the irregularity of the dorsal margin without definite scarring. Orientation as in Figure 31. (Mant case no. 7).

Figure 40. Two views of a single pair of female pubic bones (age 40, 2 children) to show the irregularity of the dorsal margin without definite scarring. Orientation as in Figure 31. (Mant case no. 8).

Selected Bibliography on Personal Identification

T. D. Stewart

As the foregoing part of the present report bears witness, a variety of special techniques are available to aid the investigator in his efforts to arrive at personal identifications. The original descriptions and modifications of these techniques are widely scattered through the medical, dental, and anthropological literature of the past century. Textbooks tend to yield distillations of this knowledge, but to refer to only a few selected sources. Also, some of the textbooks are specialized. For example, Krogman's book on *The Human Skeleton in Forensic Medicine* (1962) excludes the teeth; and Gustafson's book on *Forensic Odontology* (1966) concentrates upon the oral structures. By contrast, Reals' book on *Medical Investigation of Aviation Accidents* (1968) devotes only one chapter to the identification of bodies, and then only those from one accident. Accordingly, the accompanying bibliographies of such books are similarly restricted—even to the extent that only 0.6% of the references in Reals' book deal with identification per se. These circumstances largely account for the fact that, up to now, a wide-ranging bibliography on personal identification has been nonexistent.

Published library catalogues and periodical indexes identify articles that have a more or less direct bearing on this subject, by author, but otherwise only to the extent that the titles indicate the subject coverage. Even then the searcher is confronted with the need to look under numerous index categories, because the subject matter involves all parts of the body in varying ways and, therefore, offers numerous classificatory possibilities. That the indexers are aware of this problem, and are constantly seeking to improve their efforts, is shown by the fact that, in 1965, the *Cumulative Index Medicus* adopted the category "Forensic medicine" instead of "Identification, medico-legal," and which before that was "Jurisprudence, medical." About the same time, the *Index to the Dental Literature* introduced "Forensic dentistry" as a category. Unfortunately, neither of these major bibliographic sources fully covers the anthropological literature.

The bibliography that follows was compiled from many sources, but principally those mentioned above. An attempt was made to exclude secondary sources, but to do this fully would require examination of the contents of each item, which was not feasible. Also largely excluded were such widely known and practiced techniques as autopsy, fingerprinting, and blood-group testing. On the other hand, a large number of references to disasters has been included, because these often underscore the need for, and the success of, identification, although they seldom give the details of the methods employed. If anything, the entries are weighted heavily on the side of the skeleton, and thus reflect my own interest in this aspect of the subject. This suggests that a much better bibliography could be produced if specialists in all aspects of the subject pooled all the significant references of which they are aware. For the present, however, I can only hope that my single effort will prove useful.

1. Acheson, Roy M.
   1954. A Method of Assessing Skeletal Maturity from Radiographs. A Report from the Oxford Child Health Survey. *Journey of Anatomy,* 88:498-508.

2. Adair, F. L., and Scammon, R. E.
   1921. A Study of the Ossification of the Wrist, Knee, and Ankle at Birth, with Particular Reference to the Physical Development and Maturity of the Newborn. *American Journal of Obstetrics and Gynecology*, 2:37-60.

3. Ahlqvist, J., and Damsten, O.
   1969. A Modification of Kerley's Method for the Microscopic Determination of Age in Human Bones. *Journal of Forensic Sciences*, 14:205-12.

4. Albrook, David
   1961. The Estimation of Stature in British and East African Males. *Journal of Forensic Medicine*, 8:15-28.

5. Amoëdo, Oscar
   1897. The Role of the Dentists in the Identification of the Victims of the Catastrophe of the *Bazar de la Charité*, Paris, 4th of May, 1897. *Dental Cosmos*, 39:905-12.

6. Ancona, Fabio
   1938. Sulla determinazione dell'età mediante lo stato di obliterazione delle suture del cranio. *Archivio per l'Antropologia e Etnologia*. 68:53-114.

7. Anderson, Margaret; Messner, M. B.; and Green, W. T.
   1964. Distribution of Lengths of the Normal Femur and Tibia in Children from One to Eighteen Years of Age. *Journal of Bone and Joint Surgery*, 46A:1197-1202.

8. Ashley, David J. B.
   1959. The Technique of Nuclear Sexing. *American Journal of Clinical Pathology*, 31:230-37.

9. Ashley, G. T.
   1956. The Human Sternum; the Influence of Sex and Age on its Measurements. *Journal of Forensic Medicine*, 3(1):27-43.

10. Auteri, L.
    1940. L'onicofagia come segno d'identifizione di cadaveri corbonizzati. *Archivio di Antropologia Criminale, Psichiatria, Medicina Legale e Scienze Affini* (Torino), 60:551-57.

11. Baker, P. T., and Newman, R. W.
    1967. The Use of Bone Weight for Human Identification. *American Journal of Physical Anthropology*, 15:601-18.

12. Bambha, J. K.
    1961. Longitudinal Cephalometric Roentgenographic Study of the Face and Cranium in Relation to Body Height. *Journal of the American Dental Association*, 63:776-99.

13. Basu, S. K.
    1938. Medico-legal Aspects of the Determination of Age of Bengalese Girls. *Indian Medical Record*, 63(4):97-100.

14. Béclère, Henri
    1918a. La radiographie anthropométrique du pouce. (Superposition des empreintes digitales, du squelette et de l'ongle). *Comptes-Rendus d'Academie de Science* (Paris), 167:499-500. 30 September.

15. ————
    1918b. Le création des plans en radiographie stéréoscopique. *Comptes-Rendus d'Academie de Science* (Paris), 167:533-34. 7 October.

16. Beddoe, Harold L.
    1956. Methods of Investigation in the Identification of Human Remains. *Journal of Forensic Sciences*, 1(3):47-60.

17. Belfield, W. T.
    1923. Medico-legal Examination of Hairs. Chapter in *Legal Medicine and Toxicology*, by Peterson, Haines, and Webster, II. W. B. Saunders Co., Philadelphia.

18. Benassi, Giorgio, and Graffi, Elsa
    1923. Di un elemento per l'identification de sesso: L'indice colloideo. *Rivista Sperimentale di Freniatria e Medicina Legale delle Alienazioni Mentali* (Reggio-Emilia), 47:435-55.

19. Beresowski, A., and Lundie, J. K.
    1952. Sequence in the Time of Ossification of the Carpal Bones of 705 African Children from Birth to 6 Years of Age. *South African Journal of Medical Science*, 17:25-31.

20. Birkner, F.
    1903. Beiträge zur Rassenanatomie der Gesichtsweichteile. *Korrespondenz-blatt der deutscher Gesellschaft für Anthropologie, Ethnologie, und Urgeschichte*, 34:163-65.

21. Birkner, F.
    1905. Beiträge zur Rassenanatomie der Chinesen. *Archiv für Anthropologie,* new series, 4:1-40.

22. ———
    1907. Die Dicke der Gesichsweichteile bei verschiedenen Alter, Geschlecht und Rasse. *Sitzungsberichte der Gesellschaft für Morphologie und Physiologie,* Munich, 23(2):140-46.

23. Blair, Edward
    1964. Identification of Casualties in the Kamai Air Disaster. *New Zealand Dental Journal,* 60:151-59.

24. Blocker, Virginia, and Blocker, T. G., Jr.
    1949. The Texas City Disaster: A Survey of 3,000 Casualties. *American Journal of Surgery,* 78:756-71.

25. Blocker, T. G., Jr.; Blocker, Virginia; Graham, J. E.; and Jacobson, Herbert
    1959. Follow-up Medical Survey of the Texas City Disaster. *American Journal of Surgery,* 97:604-23.

26. Borovanský, L., and Hnévkovský
    1929. The Growth of the Body and the Process of Ossification in Prague Boys from 4 Years to 19 Years. *Anthropologie* (Prague), 7:169-208.

27. Boucher, B. J.
    1955. Sex Differences in the Foetal Sciatic Notch. *Journal of Forensic Medicine,* 2(1):51-4.

28. ———
    1957. Sex Differences in the Foetal Pelvis. *American Journal of Physical Anthropology,* 15(4):581-600.

29. Boulinier, Georges
    1968. La détermination du sexe des crânes humains à l'aide des fonctions discriminantes. *Bulletins et Mémoirs de la Société d'Antropologie de Paris,* 12th series, 3:301-16.

30. Breitinger, E.
    1937. Zur Berechnung der Körperhöhe aus den langen Gliedmassenknochen. *Anthropologischer Anzeiger,* 14(3/4):249-74.

31. Broca, Paul
    1867. Sur les proportions relatives des membres supérieurs et des membres inférieurs chez les Nègres et les Européens. *Bulletins de la Société d'Anthropologie de Paris,* 2d series, 2:641-53.

32. Brooks, Sheilagh Thompson
    1955. Skeletal Age at Death: The Reliability of Cranial and Pubic Indicators. *American Journal of Physical Anthropology,* new series, 13:567-97.

33. Brown, T. C.
    1950. Medical Identification in the Noronic Disaster. *Finger Print and Identification Magazine,* 6(32):3-14.

34. Brown, T. C.; Belaney, R. J.; and Robinson, W. L.
    1952. Medical Identification in the *Noronic* Disaster. *Journal of the American Medical Association,* 148:621-7.

35. Brues, Alice M.
    1958. Identification of Skeletal Remains. *Journal of Criminal Law, Criminology, and Police Science,* 48:551-63.

36. Cameron, J. A. P.
    1938. Estimation of Age in Asiatic Girls. *Journal of the Malaya Branch of the British Medical Association,* 2(1):19-23.

37. Carpenter, J. P.
    1968. Dental Identification of Plane Crash Victims. *Journal of the North Carolina Dental Association,* 51:9-12.

38. Ceballos, Jorge L., and Rentschler, E. H.
    1958. Roentgen Diagnosis of Sex Based on Adult Skull Characteristics; Comparison Study of Cephalometry of Male and Female Skull Films (Frontal Projection). *Radiology,* 70:55-61.

39. Christie, A.
    1949. Prevalence and Distribution of Ossification Centers in the Newborn Infant. *American Journal of Diseases of Children,* 77:355-61.

40. Clavelin, P., and Dérobert, L.
    1946. Ostéométrie anthropo-médico-légal. Volume 1: *Adolescence et âge* adulte. Balliére, Paris. 107 pages.

41. Cobb, W. Montague
    1934. Bony Gauges of Growth, Age and Disease. *Journal of the National Medical Association,* 26:121-7.

42. ———
    1952. Skeleton. Chapter 30 in *Cowdry's Problems of Ageing* (A. I. Lansing, editor), 3d edition, Williams & Wilkins Company, Baltimore. Pages 791-856.

43. Cornwell, W. S.
    1956. Radiography and Photography in Problems of Identification: A Review. *Medical Radiography and Photography,* 32(1):34-5.

44. Culbert, William L., and Law, Frederick M.
    1926. Identification of a Body by Comparison of Radiographs of the Nasal Accessory Sinuses and Mastoid Processes. *Transactions of the American Laryngological, Rhinological and Otological Society,* 32:248-50.

45. ———
    1927. Identification by Comparison of Roentgenograms of Nasal Accessory Sinuses and Mastoid Processes. *Journal of the American Medical Association,* 88(21):1634-6. 21 May.

46. Culbertson, Joe C.; Breslau, Neil A.; Moore, M. Kent; and Engel, Eric
    1969. Sex Chromatin Determination from Hair. *Journal of the American Medical Association,* 207:560-1.

47. Dahlberg, A. A.
    1957. Criteria of Individuality in the Teeth. *Journal of Forensic Sciences,* 2(4):388-401.

48. Danforth, C. H.
    1925. *Hair, with Special Reference to Hypertrichosis.* Chicago.

49. Davidson, William M., and Smith, D. Robertson
    1954. A Morphological Sex Difference in the Polymorphonuclear Neutrophil Leukocytes. *British Medical Journal,* 2:6-7.

50. Davies, D. A., and Parsons, F. G.
    1927-28. The Age Order of the Appearance and Union of the Normal Epiphyses as Seen in the X-ray. *Journal of Anatomy,* 62:58-71.

51. Dérobert, L., and Fully, G.
    1960. Étude critique de la valeur du degré d'oblitération des sutures crâniénnes pour la détermination de l'âge d'après l'examen de 480 crânes. *Annales de Médecine Légale* (Paris), 40:154-65.

52. Derry, D. E.
    1909. Note on the Innominate Bone as a Factor in the Determination of Sex: with Special Reference to the Sulcus Preauricularis. *Journal of Anatomy and Physiology,* 43 (3d series, volume 4): 266-76.

53. ———
    1912. The Influence of Sex on the Position and Composition of the Human Sacrum. *Journal of Anatomy and Physiology,* 46 (3d series, volume 7): 184-92.

54. ———
    1923. On the Sexual and Racial Characters of the Ilium. *Journal of Anatomy,* 58:71-83.

55. Deslypere, P., and Baert, H.
    1958. Assessment of Age by the Measurement of the Haversian Canals of Human Bones: A Critical Study of the Balthazard and Lebrun Method. *Journal of Forensic Medicine,* 5(4):195-9.

56. Desoille, Henri and Grinfeder
    1938. Sur l'identification des poils pouvenant de sujets de race noire. *Annales de Médecine Légale* (Paris), 18:206-12.

57. Dixon, A. D., and Torr, J. B. D.
    1956. Post-mortem Persistence of Sex Chromatin. *Journal of Forensic Medicine,* 3(4):161-8.

58. ———
    1956. Sex Chromatin as Aid to Identification of Sex in Forensic Medicine. *Nature,* London, 178:797.

59. ———
    1957. Sex Determination of Human Tissues from Cell Morphology. *Journal of Forensic Medicine,* 4(1):11-7.

60. Dokladal, Milan.
    1969. Ueber die heutigen Möglichkeiten der Personen-identifikation auf Grund von verbrannten Knocken. Experimentelle Studie. In *Aktuelle Kriminologie,* Kriminalistik Verlag, Hamburg. Pages 223-46.

61. Dorsey, George A.
    1899. The Skeleton in Medico-legal Anatomy. *Chicago Medical Recorder,* 16:172-9.

62. Duggins, Oliver H.
    1954. Age Changes in Head Hair from Birth to Maturity. IV. Refractive Indices and Birefringence of the Cuticle of the Hair of Children. *American Journal of Physical Anthropology*, new series, 12(1):89-114.
63. Dupertuis, C. W., and Hadden, J. A., Jr.
    1951. On the Reconstruction of Stature from Long Bones. *American Journal of Physical Anthropology*, new series, 9:15-54.
64. Dwight, Thomas
    1878. *The Identification of the Human Skeleton. Boston.* 54 pages.
65. ———
    1881. The Sternum as an Index of Sex and Age. *Journal of Anatomy and Physiology*, 15:327-30.
66. ———
    1890. The Sternum as an Index of Sex, Height, and Age. *Journal of Anatomy and Physiology*, 24(4):527-35.
67. ———
    1894. Methods of Estimating the Height from Parts of the Skeleton. *Medical Record*, New York, 46:293-6.
68. ———
    1904. The Size of the Articular Surfaces of the Long Bones as Characteristic of Sex; An Anthropological Study. *American Journal of Anatomy*, 4:19-31.

69. Eddy, M. W.
    1938. Hair Classification. *Proceedings of the Pennsylvania Academy of Sciences*, 12:19.
70. Eggeling, H. von
    1913. Die Leistungsfähigkeit physiognomischer Rekonstruktionsversuche auf Grundlage des Schädels. *Archiv für Anthropologie*, new series, 12:44-7.
71. Endress, Zachary F.
    1951. Radiographic Changes Following Prolonged Postmortem Exposure. *Medical Radiography and Photography*, 27(1):29-30.
72. Engel, C. E.
    1954. Superimposition. *Medical Radiography and Photography*, 30(1):20-3.
73. Ennis, L. M., and Batson, O. V.
    1936. Variations of the Maxillary Sinus as Seen in the Roentgenogram. *Journal of the American Dental Association*, 23:201-12.

74. Fanning, E. A.
    1961. A Longitudinal Study of Tooth Formation and Root Resorption. *New Zealand Dental Journal*, 57:202-17.
75. Fisher, Russell S.
    1960. Recent Developments in Forensic Pathology. *Journal of the American Medical Association*, 172(9):896-901.
76. Fisher, Russell S.; Spitz, Werner U.; Breitenecker, Rudiger; and Adams, John E.
    1965. Techniques of Identification Applied to 81 Extremely Fragmented Aircraft Fatalities. *Journal of Forensic Sciences*, 1:121-35.
77. Flecker, H.
    1942. Time of Appearance and Fusion of Ossification Centers as Observed by Roentgenographic Methods. *American Journal of Roentgenology and Radium Therapy*, 47:97-159. Reprinted in 288, pages 97-159.
78. Fontaine, Rosario
    1935. L'identification des os. Méthode histologique. *Union Médicale du Canada*, 64:1214-8.
79. Forslev, A. W.
    1966. "Nondestructive" Neutron Activation Analysis of Hair. *Journal of Forensic Sciences*, 11:217-32.
80. Francis, Carl C.
    1940. The Appearance of Centers of Ossification from 6-15 Years. *American Journal of Physical Anthropology*, 27(1):127-38.
81. ———
    1951. Appearance of Centers of Ossification in Human Pelvis Before Birth. *American Journal of Roentgenology*, 65:778-83.
82. Francis, Carl C., and Werle, Peter P.
    1939. The Appearance of Centers of Ossification from Birth to 5 Years. *American Journal of Physical Anthropology*, 24:273-99. (With the assistance of Alton Behm.)

83. Frykholm, K. O.
    1956. Identification in the *Ormen Friske* Disaster. *Acta Odontologica Scandinavica,* 14:11-21.
84. Frykholm, K. O., and Lysell, L.
    1962. Different Systems for the Recording of Teeth and Tooth Surfaces. *International Dental Journal,* 12:194-207.
85. Fully, Georges Claude
    1955. *L'identification des squelettes des déportés mort dans les camps de concentration allemands.* Thèse de Paris, 13 June. (For review, see Revue Français d'Odontostomologie, 3:501-3, 1956.)
86. Fully, Georges
    1956. Une nouvelle méthode de détermination de la taille. *Annales de Médecine Légale et de Criminologie,* 36(5):266-73.
87. Fully, G., and Dehouve, A.
    1965. Renseignements apportés dans la détermination de l'âge par l'étude anatomique et radiologique du sternum et des côtes. *Annales de Médecine Légale* (Paris), 60:145-53.
88. Fully, G., and Pineau, H.
    1960. Détermination de la stature au moyen du squelette. *Annales de Médecine Légale* (Paris), 60:145-53.
89. Fully, G.; Coblentz, A.; Dessertine, A.; et al.
    1965. Solution proposée au problème de l'identification des victimes d'accident d'avion (traffic international). *Annales de Médecine Légale* (Paris), 45:257-64.

90. Galton, Francis
    1888. Personal Identification and Description. *Nature* (London), 38:173-7, 201-2. Reprinted in *Journal of the Anthropological Institute of Great Britain and Ireland,* 18:177-91.
91. Garn, S. M.
    1951a. Types and Distribution of Hair in Man. *Annals of the New York Academy of Sciences,* 53(3):498-507.
92. ———
    1951b. The Examination of Head Hair under the Polarizing Microscope. *Annals of the New York Academy of Sciences,* 53(3):649-52.
93. Garn, S. M.; Lewis, A. B.; Koski, Kalevi; and Polacheck, D. L.
    1958. The Sex Difference in Tooth Calcification. *Journal of Dental Research,* 37:561-7.
94. Genovés T., Santiago
    1959. Diferencias sexuales en el hueso coxal. *Universidad Nacional Autonoma de México. Publicaciones del Instituto de Historia.* Primary series, number 49.
95. ———
    1967. Proportionality of the Long Bones and Their Relation to Stature Among Mesoamericans. *American Journal of Physical Anthropology,* 26:67-77.
96. Gerasimov, M. M.
    1955. Vosstanovlenie lit͡sa po cherepu [Reconstruction of the Face on the Skull]. *Akademiia Nauk, SSSR, Trudy Institut Ethnografii,* new series, volume 28.
97. ———
    1962. Reconstitution du visage d'après de crâne. Actes du VI*e* Congrès International des Sciences Anthropologiques et Ethnologiques (Paris, 1960), 1:175-7.
98. Giles, E.
    1964. Sex Determination by Discriminant Function Analysis of the Mandible. *American Journal of Physical Anthropology,* 22:129-35.
99. ———
    1966. Statistical Techniques for Sex and Race Determination; Some Comments in Defense. *American Journal of Physical Anthropology,* 25:85-6.
100. Giles, Eugene, and Elliott, Orville
    1962a. Negro-White Identification from the Skull. *Actes du VI*e* Congrès International des Sciences Anthropologiques et Ethnologiques* (Paris, 1960), 1:179-84.
101. ———
    1962b. Race Identification from Cranial Measurements. *Journal of Forensic Sciences,* 7(2):147-57.
102. ———
    1963. Sex Determination by Discriminant Function Analysis of Crania. *American Journal of Physical Anthropology,* 21:53-68.
103. Glaister, J.
    1931. *Monograph on Hairs of Mammalia Considered from Medico-Legal Aspect.* Publication of the Egyptian Government.

104. Gleiser, I., and Hunt, E. E., Jr.
   1955. The Permanent Mandibular First Molar: Its Calcification, Eruption, and Decay. *American Journal of Physical Anthropology,* 13:253-83.
105. Godycki, M.
   1957. Sur la certitude de détermination de sexe d'après le fémur, le cubitus, et l'humérus. *Bulletins et Mémoirs de la Société d'Anthropologie de Paris,* series 10, 8:405-10.
106. Gollin, K.
   1927. *Ueber die Unterscheidung menschlicher und tierischer Knochenfunde.* Dietenheim, 41 pages.
107. Grant, Edmund, A.; Prendergast, W. K.; and White, E. A.
   1952. Dental Identification in the *Noronic* Disaster. *Journal of the Canadian Dental Association,* 18(1):3-18.
108. Grass, E.
   1916. *Untersuchungen zur Frage der Differentialdiagnose zwischen Menschen- und Tierknochen.* Berlin. 21 pages.
109. Graves, W. W.
   1922. Observations on Age Changes in the Scapula. A Preliminary Note. *American Journal of Physical Anthropology.* 5:21-34. Reprinted in 288, pages 245-63.
110. Gray, S. W., and Lamons, F. P.
   1959. Skeletal Development and Tooth Eruption in Atlanta Children. *American Journal of Orthodontics,* 45:272-7.
111. Greenwell, M. D.; Willner, A.; and Kirk, Paul L.
   1941. Human Hair Studies. III. Refractive Index of Crown Hair. *Journal of Criminal Law and Criminology,* 31:746-52.
112. Greulich, W. W.
   1960a. Value of X-ray Films of Hand and Wrist in Human Identification. *Science,* 131:155-6.
113. ———
   1960b. Skeletal Features Visible on the Roentgenogram of Hand and Wrist Which Can Be Used for Establishing Individual Identification. *American Journal of Roentgenology, Radium Therapy and Nuclear Medicine,* 83(4):756-64.
114. Greulich, William Walter, and Pyle, S. Idell
   1959. *Radiographic Atlas of Skeletal Development of the Hand and Wrist.* 2d edition. Stanford University Press.
115. Grob, H. S., and Kupperman, H. S.
   1961. Experiences with Techniques of Chromatin Sex Determination. *American Journal of Clinical Pathology,* 36:132-8.
116. Gross, E. M., and Blumberg, J. M.
   1966. Identification and Injuries of Air-Crash Victims. *Archives of Environmental Health* (Chicago), 13:289-91.
117. Gustafson, G.
   1947. Microscopic Examination of Teeth as a Means of Identification in Forensic Medicine. *Journal of American Dental Association,* 35:720-4.
118. ———
   1950. Age Determinations on Teeth. *Journal of American Dental Association,* 41:45-54.
119. Gustafson, Gösta
   1966. *Forensic Odontology.* American Alsevier Publishing Company, Inc., New York.
120. Gustafson, Gösta, and Johanson, Gunnar
   1963. The Value of Certain Characteristics in Dental Identification. *Acta Odontologica Scandinavica,* 21:367-89.

121. Haeusermann, E.
   1925-26. Zur Bestimmung von Geschlechts- und Rassenunterschieden am menschlichen Os ilium durch Messung. *Zeitschrift für Morphologie und Anthropologie,* 25:465-74.
122. Haines, D. H.
   1967. Dental Identification in the Stockport Air Disaster. *British Dental Journal,* 123:336-8.
123. Hall, M.
   1898. Ueber Gesichtsbildung. *Mitteilungen der anthropologische Gesellschaft in Wein,* 28:57-100.
124. Hanihara, Kazuro
   1952. [Age Changes in the Male Japanese Pubic Bone.] *Zinruigaku Zassi* (Journal of the Anthropological Society, Nippon), 62(698):245-60. (In Japanese, with English summary.)

125. Hanihara, Kazuro
    1958. [Sexual Diagnosis of Japanese Long Bones by Means of Discriminant Function.] *Zinruigaku Zassi* (Journal of the Anthropological Society, Nippon), 66(717):187-96. (In Japanese, with English summary.)

126. ————
    1959. [Sex Diagnosis of Japanese Skulls and Scapulae by Means of Discriminant Function.] *Zinruigaku Zassi* (Journal of the Anthropological Society, Nippon), 67(722):191-7. (In Japanese, with English summary.)

127. Hanihara, K.; Kimura, K.; and Minamidate, T.
    1964. [The Sexing of Japanese Skeletons by Means of Discriminant Function.] *Nihon Hôigaku Zassi* (Japanese Journal of Legal Medicine), 18:107-14. (In Japanese, with English summary.)

128. Hanna, Robert E., and Washburn, S. L.
    1953. The Differentiation of the Sex of Skeletons, as Illustrated by a Study of the Eskimo Pelvis. *Human Biology*, 24(1):21-7.

129. Hansen, Gerhard
    1953-54. Die Altersbestimmung am proximalen Humerus- und Femurende in Rahmen der Identifizierung menschlicher Skelettreste. *Wissenschaftliche Zeitschrift der Humboldt-Universität zu Berlin. Mathematish-Naturwissenschaftliche Reihe*, number 1, volume 3, pages 1-73.

130. Harmeling, G. L.; Schuh, E.; and Humphreys, H. S.
    1968. Dental Identification of Bodies in a Major Disaster. *South Carolina Dental Journal*, 26(7):4-11 (pages out of order).

131. Hausman, L. A.
    1920. Structural Characteristics of the Hair of Mammals. *American Naturalist*, 54:496-523.

132. ————
    1925a. A Comparative Racial Study of the Structural Elements of Human Head-hair. *American Naturalist*, 59:529-38.

133. ————
    1925b. The Relationships of the Microscopic Structural Characters of Human Head-hair. *American Journal of Physical Anthropology*, 8:173-7.

134. ————
    1927. The Pigmentation of Human Head-hair. *American Naturalist*, 61:545-54.

135. ————
    1932. The Cortical Fusi of Mammalian Hair Shafts. *American Naturalist*, 66:461-70.

136. ————
    1934. Histological Variability of Human Hair. *American Journal of Physical Anthropology*, 18:415-29.

137. Henrikson, Carl Oskar; Söremark, Rune; and Frykholm, K. O.
    1962. The Use of an Iodine-125 X-ray Unit in Forensic Odontology. *Odontologisk Revy* (Malmö), 13:130-8.

138. Hepworth, S. M.
    1929. On the Determination of Age in Indians, from a Study of the Ossification of the Epiphyses of the Long Bones. *Indian Medical Gazette*, 64:128.

139. Hill, Alfred H.
    1939. Fetal Age Assessment by Centers of Ossification. *American Journal of Physical Anthropology*, 24:251-72.

140. Hoerr, Normand L., and Pyle, S. Idell.
    1962. *Radiographic Atlas of Skeletal Development of the Foot and Ankle*. Charles C Thomas, Springfield, Illinois.

141. Holl, M.
    1898. Ueber Gesichtsbildung. *Mitteilungen der anthropologische Gesellschaft*, Wien, 28:57-100.

142. Holzer, F. J., and Patscheider, H.
    1966. Die Flugzeugkatastrophe. *Deutsche Zeitschrift für de gesamte gerichtliche Medizin* (Berlin), 57:133-44.

143. Hooton, E. A.
    1943. Medico-legal Aspects of Physical Anthropology. *Clinics*, 1:1612-24.

144. Hörberg, E., and Johanson, G.
    1963. [Co-operation between Police and Dentist in the Identification of the Victims of a Fire in Malmö]. *Nordisk Kriminalteknisk Tidskrift*, 33:215-24. (In Norwegian.)

145. Howells, W. W.
    1964. Détermination du sexe du bassin par fonction discriminante: Étude du matériel du Docteur Gaillard. *Bulletins et Mémoires de la Société d'Anthropologie de Paris*, 11th series, 7:95-105.

146. Hunt, E. E., Jr., and Gleiser, I.
    1955. The Estimation of Age and Sex of Preadolescent Children from Bones and Teeth. *American Journal of Physical Anthropology,* 13(3):479-87.
147. Hurme, V. O.
    1948. Standards of Variation in the Eruption of the First Six Permanent Teeth. *Child Development,* 19(4):213-31. Reprinted, with the addition of a diagram, in *Yearbook of Physical Anthropology for 1948,* 4:181-200, New York, 1949; also reprinted in 288, pages 35-53.
148. ———
    1949. Ranges of Normalcy in the Eruption of Permanent Teeth. *Journal of Dentistry for Children,* 16:11-5.
149. ———
    1957. Time and Sequence of Tooth Eruption. *Journal of Forensic Sciences,* 2(4):377-88.
150. Iordanidis, P.
    1961a. Détermination du sexe par les os du squelette (Crâne). *Annales de Médecine Légale* (Paris), 41:23-34.
151. ———
    1961b. Détermination du sexe par les os du squelette (Atlas, axis, clavicule, omoplate, sternum). *Annales de Médecine Légale* (Paris), 41:280-91.
152. ———
    1961c. Détermination du sexe par les os du squelette (os coxal et sacrum). *Annales de Médecine Légale* (Paris), 41:347-58.
153. ———
    1961d. Détermination du sexe par les os du squelette (Fémur, tibia, humérus, radius, cubitus, astragale, calcanéum). *Annales de Médecine Légale* (Paris), 41:459-71.
154. Jit, I., et al.
    1966. The Sexing of the Adult Clavicles. *Indian Journal of Medical Research,* 54: 551-71.
155. Johannsen, J.
    1960. [The Fire Catastrophe on the Haderslev Estuary on July 8th, 1959, and the Subsequent Identification.] *Nordisk Kriminalteknisk Tidskrift,* 30:149-56. (In Norwegian.)
156. Johanson, Gunnar, and Saldeen, Tom
    1969. Identification of Burnt Victims with the Aid of Tooth and Bone Fragments. *Journal of Forensic Medicine,* 16:16-25.
157. ———
    1969. A New Method for the Radiological Detection and Identification of Fragments of Teeth and Bone Recovered from Burnt Victims. *Journal of Forensic Medicine,* 16:26-8.
158. Johnson, C. C.
    1968. Transparent Dentine in Age Estimation. *Oral Surgery,* 25:834-8.
159. Kajanoja, P.
    1966. Sex Determination of Finnish Crania by Discriminant Function Analysis. *American Journal of Physical Anthropology,* 24:29-33.
160. Keen, E. N.
    1953. Estimation of Stature from the Long Bones. A Discussion of its Reliability. *Journal of Forensic Medicine,* 1(1):46-51.
161. Keen, J. A.
    1950. A Study of the Differences Between Male and Female Skulls. *American Journal of Physical Anthropology, new series,* 8(1):65-79.
162. Keiser-Nielsen, Sören
    1951a. [Dental Identification of Danish Patriots Who Died in German Concentration Camps.] *Odontologisk Tidskrift* (Goteborg), 59:57-69. (In Danish, with English summary.)
163. ———
    1951b. [Dental Identification of Victims from an Air Accident.] *Odontologisk Tidskrift* (Goteborg), 59:70-9. (In Danish, with English summary.)
164. ———
    1963a. Dental Investigation in Mass Disasters. *Journal of Dental Research,* 42(1, part 2):303-11.
165. ———
    1965. Geographic Factors in Forensic Odontology. *International Dental Journal,* 15:343-7.

166. Keiser-Nielsen, S.; Frykholm, K. O.; and Ström, F.
    1964. Identification of Unknown Bodies. Procedures Used in Scandinavia, Emphasizing Odontological Aspects. *International Dental Journal,* 14(3):317-29.
167. Kerley, Ellis R.
    1965. The Microscopic Determination of Age in Human Bone. *American Journal of Physical Anthropology,* 23(2):149-63.
168. ———
    1969. Age Determination of Bone Fragments. *Journal of Forensic Sciences,* 14:59-67.
169. Kind, S. S.
    1965. Metrical Characters in the Identification of Animal Hairs. *Journal of Forensic Sciences,* 5:110-1.
170. Kirk, Paul L.
    1940. Human Hair Studies. I. General Considerations of Hair Individualization and its Forensic Importance. *Journal of Criminal Law and Criminology,* 31:486-96.
171. Knott, N. J.
    1967. Identification by the Teeth of Casualties in the Aberfan Disaster. *British Dental Journal,* 122:144-5.
172. Kollmann, J.
    1898. Die Weichteile des Gesichts und die Persistenz der Rassen. *Anthrologischer Anzeiger,* 15(10):165-77.
173. Kollmann, J., and Buechly, W.
    1898. Die Persistenze der Rassen und die Reconstruction der Physiognomie in prähistorischer Schädel. *Archiv für Anthropologie,* 25:329-59.
174. Krogman, Wilton M.
    1939. A Guide to the Identification of Human Skeletal Material. *FBI Law Enforcement Bulletin,* 8:1-29.
175. ———
    1943. Role of the Physical Anthropologist in the Identification of Human Skeletal Remains. *FBI Law Enforcement Bulletin,* 12(4):17-29.
176. ———
    1946. The Reconstruction of the Living Head from the Skull. *FBI Law Enforcement Bulletin,* 15:11-8. (With Miss M. J. McCue.)
177. ———
    1949. The Human Skeleton in Legal Medicine. In *Symposium on Medicolegal Problems,* S. A. Levinson, editor, pages 1-92. J. B. Lippincott Company, Philadelphia.
178. ———
    1962a. A Problem in the Ageing of Human Skeletal Remains. *Journal of Forensic Sciences* 7(3): 255-64.
179. ———
    1962b. *The Human Skeleton in Forensic Medicine.* Charles C Thomas, Springfield, Illinois.
180. Kronfeld, Rudolf
    1935. Development and Calcification of the Human Deciduous and Permanent Dentition. *The Bur,* 35(1):18-25. Reprinted in 288, pages 3-10.
181. Krukierek, Stanisław.
    1951. The Sexual Differences of the Human Pelvis. *Gynaecologia,* 132:92-110.
182. Kurth, G.
    1950. Ueber die Verwendbarkeit der Grablänge vor- und frühgeschichtlicher Reihengräberserien zur Bestimmung einer genauen Körperhöhe. *Zeitschrift für Morphologie und Anthropologie,* 42:293-306.
183. Lall, R., and Townsend R. S.
    1939. Ages of Epiphysial Union at Elbow and Wrist Joints Amongst Indian Girls. *Indian Medical Gazette,* 74:614-16.
184. Lasker, Gabriel W., and Lee, Marjorie M. C.
    1957. Racial Traits in the Human Teeth. *Journal of Forensic Sciences,* 2(4):401-19.
185. Laufer, Berthold
    1913. History of the Finger-Print System. *Smithsonian Annual Report for 1912,* 631-52,
186. Law, Frederick M.
    1934. Roentgenograms as a Means of Identification. *American Journal of Surgery,* 26:195-8.
187. Lochte, T.
    1938. *Atlas der menschlichen und tierschen Haare.* Paul Schops, Leizpig. 306 pages.
188. López Alonzo, Sergio
    1969. Funciones discriminantes en la determinación sexual de huesos largos. *Museo Nacional de Anthropologia, México, Anthropologia-Matemática,* number 12. (Mimeograph.)

189. Luntz, L. L.
1967. Dental Radiography and Photography in Identification. *Dental Radiography and Photography,* 40:7884 passim.

190. Mackay, D. H.
1952. Skeletal Maturation in the Hand: A Study of Development of East African Children. *Transactions Royal Society of Tropical Medicine and Hygiene,* 46: 135-42.

191. Mann, G. T.; Karnitschnig, H. H.; Beddoe, H. L.; Enos, W. E.; Homes, R. H.; and Beyer, J. C.
1965. The Identification of Mass Aircrash Victims. *Medico-legal Bulletin,* 142:1-6 (Mimeograph.)

192. Mant, A. K.
1962. The Identification of Mutilated and Decomposed Bodies (with Special Reference to Air Crash Victims.) *Medicine, Science, and the Law,* 2:134-42.

193. Maresh, Marion M.
1940. Paranasal Sinuses from Birth to Late Adolescence. I. Size of the Paranasal Sinuses as Observed in Routine Posteroanterior Roentgenograms. *American Journal of Diseases of Children,* 60:55-78.

194. Matzdorff
1935. Fettwachsbildung. *Deutsche Zeitschrift fur de gesamte gerichtliche Medizin* (Berlin), 24:246-9.

195. Mayer, J.
1935. Identification by Sinus Prints. *Virginia Medical Monthly,* 62:517-9.

196. McKern, Thomas W.
1957. Estimation of Skeletal Age from Combined Maturational Activity. *American Journal of Physical Anthropology,* 15:399-408.

197. McKern, Thomas W., and Stewart, T. D.
1957. Skeletal Age Changes in Young American Males, Analyzed from the Standpoint of Age Identification. *Technical Report EP-45,* Environmental Protection Research Division, Quartermaster Research and Development Center, U.S. Army, Natick, Massachusetts.

198. Mendes-Corrêa, A. A.
1932. La taille des Portugais d'après les os longs. *Anthropologie,* Prague, 10:268-72.

199. Meredith, Howard V.
1946. Order and Age of Eruption for the Deciduous Dentition. *Journal of Dental Research,* 25:43-66. Reprinted in 288, pages 11-34.

200. Mercer, J. O.; Reid, J. D.; and Uttley, K. F. M.
1954. The Identification of Exhumed Bodies; a Brief Report of the Exhumation of the Unidentified Dead after the Tangiwai Railway Accident. *New Zealand Medical Journal,* 53: 329-34.

201. Merkel, H.
1931. Diagnostische Feststellungsmöglichkeiten bei verbrannten und verkohlten menschlichen Leichen. *Deutsche Zeitschrift für de gesamte gerichtliche Medizin* (Berlin), 18:232-49.

202. Miles, A. E. W.
1958. The Assessment of Age from the Dentition. *Proceedings of the Royal Society of Medicine, Section on Odontology,* 51:1057-60.

203. ———
1963. Dentition in the Estimation of Age. *Journal of Dental Research,* 42(1, part 2): 255-63.

204. Minnich, J. T.
1967. The FBI's Disaster Squad. *Medico-Legal Journal,* 35:119-29.

205. Moore, K. L. and Barr, M. L.
1954. Nuclear Morphology According to Sex, in Human Tissues. *Acta Anatomica,* 21:197-208.

206. Morgan, T. Addison, and Harris, Mary Cary
1953. The Use of X-rays as an Aid to Medico-legal Investigation. *Journal of Forensic Medicine,* 1(1):28-38.

207. Morisot, J.
1925. *L'identification par les dents.* Paris.

208. Moritz, A. R.
1939. The Cuticular Scales of Hair. Chapter (pages 110-18) in *Recent Advances in Forensic Medicine,* edited by Smith & Glaister. 2d edition.

209. Morovic-Budak, Anka
1965. Experiences in the Process of Putrefaction in Corpses Buried in Earth. *Medicine, Science, and the Law,* 5:40-3.

210. Müller, Gertrude

1935. Zur Bestimmung der Länge beschädigter Extremitatenknochen. *Anthropologischer Anzeiger,* 12:70-2.

211. Murashima, M., et al.

1964. [Attempts at Establishing a Reasonable Resemblance to the Original Person in the Photograph (of the Deceased during Life) from the Moulage of the Unknown Skull with Modeling Clay.] *Journal of the Tokyo Medical College,* 22:427-36. (In Japanese.)

212. Nat, B. S.

1931. Estimation of Stature from Long Bones in Indians of the United Provinces; Medico-legal Inquiry in Anthropometry. *Indian Journal of Medical Research,* 18:1245-53.

213. Neiss, Axel

1962. Röntgen-identification. *Wehrmedizinische Mitteilungen,* 49-52.

214. Nortömme, H. L., and Ström, F.

1946. [The Exhumation and Identification of 183 Victims Executed by the Germans in Norway.] *Nordisk Kriminalteknisk Tidskrift,* 16:13-21 (In Norwegian.)

215. ———

1946. Exhumation and Identification of the Bodies of 183 Persons Executed by the Germans at Trandum (Norway). *International Criminal Police Review,* (English edition), 1(3):7-14.

216. Olikhoff, S. A.

1904. [Microscopical Differentiation of Human from Animal Bones] *Vestnik Obshtshestvennoi Higienî, Sudebnoĭ i Prakticheskoĭ Meditsiny,* Saint Petersburg. Part 2, pages 352-62. (In Russian.)

217. Olivier, G., and Pineau, H.

1957. Détermination du sexe par les poids des os. *Bulletins et Mémoires de la Société d'Anthropologie,* Paris. Series 10, 9:328-39.

218. ———

1960. Nouvelle détermination de la taille foetale d'après les longueurs diaphysaires des os longs. *Annales de Médecine Légale,* Paris, 40:41-4.

219. Pan, N.

1924. Length of Long Bones and Their Proportion to Body Height in Hindus. *Journal of Anatomy,* London, 58:374-8.

220. Pearson, K.

1899. IV. Mathematical Contributions to the Theory of Evolution. V. On the Reconstruction of the Stature of Prehistoric Races. *Philosophical Transactions of the Royal Society,* series A, 192:169-244.

221. Pearson, Karl

1915. On the Problem of Sexing Osteometric Material. *Biometrika,* 10:479-87.

222. Pearson, Karl, and Bell, Julia

1919. *A Study of the Long Bones of the English Skeleton.* In two parts (separate atlas, dated 1917). Cambridge University Press, London.

223. Pedersen, P. A., and Scott, D. B.

1951. Replica Studies of the Surfaces of Teeth from Alaskan Eskimo, West Greenland Natives, and American Whites, *Acta Odontologica Scandinavica,* 9:262-92.

224. Perkons, A. K., and Jervis, R. E.

1962. Application of Radio-activation Analysis in Forensic Investigations. *Journal of Forensic Sciences,* 7(4):449-64.

225. ———

1966. Trace Elements in Human Head Hair. *Journal of Forensic Sciences,* 11(1):50-63.

226. Peterson, H.

1930. Die Underscheidung von Tier- und Menschenknochen. In *Handbuch der mikroscopischen Anatomie des Menschen* by W. Möllendorff. Julius Springer, Berlin, 2(2):639.

227. Phenice, T. W.

1969. A Newly Developed Visual Method of Sexing the Os Pubis. *American Journal of Physical Anthropology,* 30:297-301.

228. Phillips, R. B., and McKee, D. L.

1952. The Identification and Handling of the Dead. *U.S. Armed Forces Medical Journal,* 3:1341-6.

229. Pons, José

1955. The Sexual Diagnosis of Isolated Bones of the Skeleton. *Human Biology,* 27(1):12-21.

230. Pryor, J. W.
1923. Differences in the Time of Development of Centers of Ossification in the Male and Female Skeleton. *Anatomical Record*, 25(5):257-73.

231. ———
1928. Difference in the Ossification of the Male and Female Skeleton. *Journal of Anatomy*, London, 62:499-506.

232. ———
1933. Roentgenographic Investigation of the Time Element in Ossification. *American Journal of Roentgenology*, 28:798-804.

233. Pyle, S. Idell, and Hoerr, Normand L.
1955. *Radiographic Atlas of Skeletal Development of the Knee.* Charles C Thomas, Springfield, Illinois.

234. Reals, William J. (editor)
1968. *Medical Investigation of Aviation Accidents.* College of American Pathologists, Chicago, Illinois.

235. Rogers, A. P.
1936. Identification by Dental Means. *Journal of the American Dental Association*, 23:181-9.

236. Rollet, Étienne
1888. *De la mensuration des os longs des membres dan ses rapports avec l'anthropologie, la clinique et la médicine judiciare.* Lyon. 128 pages.

237. Ronchese, Franceso
1945. Calluses, Cicatrices and Other Stigmas as an Aid to Personal Identification. *Journal of the American Medical Association*, 128:925-32.

238. ———
1948. *Occupational Marks and Other Physical Signs: A Guide to Personal Identification.* Grune & Stratton, Inc., New York. 181 pages.

239. Salley, J. J.; Filipowicz, F. J.; and Karnitschnig, H. H.
1963. Dental Identification of Mass Disaster Victims. *Journal of the American Dental Association:* 66:827-32.

240. Sassouni, Viken
1957. Palatoprint, Physioprint, and Roentgenographic Cephalometry as New Methods in Human Identification (Preliminary Report) *Journal of Forensic Sciences*, 2(4):428-42.

241. ———
1958. Physical Individuality and the Problem of Identification. *Temple University Law Quarterly*, 31:341-51.

242. ———
1959. Cephalometric Identification. A Proposed Method of Identification of War Dead by Means of Roentgenographic Cephalometry. *Journal of Forensic Sciences*, 4(1):1-10.

243. ———
1960. Identification of War Dead by Means of Roentgenographic Cephalometry. *Technical Report EP-125*, Environmental Protection Research Division, Quartermaster Research and Engineering Center, Natick, Massachusetts. 65 pages.

244. ———
1963. Dentofacial Radiography in Forensic Dentistry. *Journal of Dental Research*, 42 (1, part 2):274-302.

245. Sauter, M.-R. and Privat, F.
1952. Une nouvelle méthode de détermination sexuelle de l'os coxal: l'indice cotylo sciatique. *Bulletin des Schweizersche Gesellschaft für Anthropologie und Ethnologie*, 28:12-3.

246. Scammon, Richard E.
1937. Two Simple Nomographs for Estimating the Age and Some of the Major External Dimensions of the Human Fetus. *Anatomical Record*, 68:221-5.

247. Schmid, W.
1967. Sex Chromatin in Hair Roots. *Cytogenetics*, 6: 342-9.

248. Schouruf, Kay
1949. Expérience sur l'exhumation de cadavres vieux de 2 à 4 ans. *Acta Medicinae Legalis et Socialis* (Liège), 2:211-24. (With English summary.)

249. ———
1950. Exhumation et identification des cadavres de prisonniers danois morts dans les camps de concentration allemands. *Acta Medicinae Legalis et Socialis* (Liège), 3:41-54. (With English summary.)

250. Schranz, D.
     1933. Der Oberarmknochen und seine gerichtlichmedizinische Bedeutung aus dem Gesichtspunkte der Identität. *Deutsche Zeitschrift für des gesamte gerichtliche Medizin* (Berlin) 22:332-61.

251. ———
     1959. Age Determinations from the Internal Structure of the Humerus. *American Journal of Physical Anthropology*, 17(4):273-8.

252. Schüller, Arthur
     1921. Das Röntgenogram der Stirnhöhle: Ein Hilfsmittel für die Identitätsbestimmung von Schädeln. *Monatschrift für Ohrenheilkunde und Laryngo-Rhinologie* (Wien), 55:1617-20.

253. ———
     1943. Note on the Identification of Skulls by X-ray Pictures of the Frontal Sinuses. *Medical Journal of Australia*, 1:554-6.

254. Scott, D. B.
     1963. Laboratory Investigation of Fragmentary Medicolegal Specimens. *Journal of Dental Research*, 42(1, part 2):317-9.

255. Scott, David B.; Kaplan, Harry; and Wycoff, Ralph W. G.
     1949. Replica Studies of Changes in Tooth Surfaces with Age. *Journal of Dental Research*, 28(1):31-47.

256. Sedwick, H. J.
     1934. Form, Size, and Position of the Maxillary Sinus at Various Ages Studied by Means of Roentgenograms of the Skull. *American Journal of Roentgenology*, 32:154-60.

257. Seibert, Henri C., and Steggerda, Morris.
     1942. The Size and Shape of Human Head-hair. *Journal of Heredity*, 33:302-4.

258. Shibata, M.; Hirota, T.; Tsuruzono, M.; Teraniski, N.; Narita, N.; Yamamoto, H.; and Kita, H.
     1963. [Estimation of Age of Victims from Pieces of Their Organs. I. The Speen. 1. The Thickness of the Capsule of the Human Speen]. *Japanese Journal of Legal Medicine,* 17:75-82. (In Japanese.)

259. Shibata, M.; Narita, N.; Hirota, T.; Tsuruzono, M.; Teraniski, N.; Uehara, M.; Yamamoto, H.; and Kita, H.
     1963. [Estimation of Age of Victims from Pieces of Their Organs. II. The Lungs. 1. Anthracosis]. *Japanese Journal of Legal Medicine,* 17:83-102. (In Japanese.)

260. Silva, Luiz
     1934. Identificação dos estygmas dentarios profissionaes. *Arquivos de Medicina Legal e Identificação* (Rio de Janeiro) 4(10):174-9.

261. Simonin, C.
     1948. Identification des corps des soldats Americains inconnus. *Acta Medicinae Legalis et Socialis* (Liège), 1:382-6.

262. Singer, Ronald
     1953. Estimation of Age from Cranial Suture Closure. A Report on its Unreliability. *Journal of Forensic Medicine*, 1(1):52-9.

263. Singleton, A. C.
     1951. The Roentgenological Identification of Victims of the *Noronic* Disaster. *American Journal of Roentgenology and Radium Therapy*, 66(3):375-84.

264. Snow, Charles E.
     1948. The Identification of the Unknown War Dead. *American Journal of Physical Anthropology*, new series, 6:323-8.

265. Spann, W.
     1959. Das Flugzengunglück in München-Riem am 6.2.1958. Pathologisch-anatomische Ergebnisse. *Münchener medizinische Wokenschrift*, 101:511-7.

266. Stack, Maurice V.
     1960. Forensic Estimation of Age in Infancy by Gravimetric Observations on the Developing Dentition. *Journal of the Forensic Science Society* (London), 1:49-59.

267. Stadtmüller, Franz
     1921-25. Zur Beurteilung der plastischen Rekonstruktionsmethode der Physiognomie auf dem Schädel. *Zeitschrift für Morphologie und Anthropologie*, 22:337-72; 23:301-14.

268. Steel, F. L. D.
     1958. The Sex of Isolated Femora. *Journal of Anatomy*, London, 92:653. (Abstract.)

269. ———
     1960. Investigation of Skeletal Remains of a Known Population. *Medicine, Science, and the Law*, 1:54-62.

270. Steel, F. L. D.
    1962. The Sexing of Long Bones, with Reference to the St. Bride's Series of Identified Skeletons. *Journal of the Royal Anthropological Institute,* 92:212-22.

271. ———
    1966. Further Observations on the Osteometric Discriminant Function. The Human Clavicle. *American Journal of Physical Anthropology,* 25:319-22.

272. Steele, D. Gentry, and McKern, Thomas W.
    1969. A Method for Assessment of Maximum Long Bone Length and Living Stature from Fragmentary Long Bones. *American Journal of Physical Anthropology,* 31:215-27.

273. Steggerda, Morris, and Seibert, Henri C.
    1941. Size and Shape of Head Hair from Six Racial Groups. *Journal of Heredity,* 32:315-9.

274. Stevens, P. J.
    1965. Practical Problems Arising in the Investigation of Airline Disasters Abroad. *Aerospace Medicine,* 36:641-6.

275. Stevens, P. J., and Tarlton, S. W.
    1963. Identification of Mass Casualties. Experience in Four Civil Air Disasters. *Medicine, Science, and the Law,* 3:154-68.

276. Stevens, P. J., et al.
    1966. Medical Investigation in Fatal Aircraft Accidents. The Role of Dental Evidence. *British Dental Journal,* 120:263-70.

277. Stevenson, Paul H.
    1924. Age Order of Epiphyseal Union in Man. *American Journal of Physical Anthropology,* 7(1):53-93. Reprinted in 288, pages 55-95.

278. ———
    1929. On Racial Differences in Stature Long Bone Regression Formulae, with Special Reference to Stature Reconstruction Formulae for the Chinese. *Biometrika,* 21:303-21.

279 Stewart, T. D.
    1934. Sequence of Epiphyseal Union, Third Molar Eruption and Suture Closure in Eskimos and American Indians. *American Journal of Physical Anthropology,* 19:433-52.

280. ———
    1953. Research in Human Identification. *Science,* 118:3 (28 August.)

281. ———
    1954a. Metamorphosis of the Joints of the Sternum in Relation to Age Changes in Other Bones. *American Journal of Physical Anthropology,* new series, 12(4): 519-36.

282. ———
    1954b. Sex Determination of the Skeleton by Guess and by Measurement. *American Journal of Physical Anthropology,* new series, 12(3):385-92.

283. ———
    1957. Distortion of the Pubic Symphyseal Surface in Females and its Effect on Age Determination. *American Journal of Physical Anthropology,* 15(1):9-18.

284. ———
    1958. The Rate of Development of Vertebral Osteoarthritis in American Whites and Its Significance in Skeletal Age Identification. *The Leech,* Johannesburg, 28(3-5):144-51.

285. ———
    1962. Anterior Femoral Curvature: Its Utility for Race Identification. *Human Biology,* 34(1):49-62.

286. ———
    1963. New Developments in Evaluating Evidence from the Skeleton. *Journal of Dental Research,* 42(1, part 2):264-73.

287. ———
    1968. Identification by Skeletal Structures. Chapter 11 (pages 123-54) in *Gradwohl's Legal Medicine,* 2d edition (edited by Francis E. Camps). John Wright & Sons, Ltd., Bristol.

288. Stewart, T. D., and Trotter, M. (editors)
    1954. *Basic Readings on the Identification of Human Skeletons: Estimation of Age.* Wenner-Gren Foundation for Anthropological Research, Inc., New York.

289. Ström, Ferdinand
    1943 [The Identification of Victims after Bombing.] *Nordisk Kriminalteknisk Tidskrift,* 13:153-6 (In Norwegian.)

290. Ström, Ferdinand
    1956. [An Air Accident—the Identification of the Victims]. *Norske Tannlaegeforennigs Tidende,* 66:553-63. (In Norwegian.)

291. Ström, F., and Toverud, G.
    1940. Die Brandkatastrophe in Oslo, 1938 und die Ergebnisse der Fixierung der Verunglückten. *Deutsche Zahn-, Mund- und Kieferheilkunde,* 7(12):720-32.

292. Suk, V.
    1935. Fallacies of Anthropological Identifications and Reconstructions. A Critique Based on Anatomical Dissection. *Publications de la Faculté des Sciences de l'Université Masaryk,* Brno, 207:1-18.

293. Sutow, Wataru W.
    1953. Skeletal Maturation in Healthy Japanese Children, 6 to 19 Years of Age; Comparison with Skeletal Maturation in American Children. *Hiroshima Journal of Medical Science,* 2:181-91.

294. Suzuki, Hisashi
    1948. On the Thickness of the Facial Soft Parts in the Japanese. *Journal of the Anthropological Society, Nippon.* 60(687):7-11. (In Japanese.)

295. Telkkä, A.
    1950. On the Prediction of Human Stature from the Long Bones. *Acta Anatomica,* 9:103-17.

296. Telkkä, Antti; Palkama, Arto; and Virtama, Pekka
    1962. Prediction of Stature from Radiographs of Long Bones in Children. *Journal of Forensic Sciences,* 7(4):474-9.

297. Thieme, Frederick, P.
    1957. Sex in Negro Skeletons. *Journal of Forensic Medicine,* 4(2):72-81.

298. Thieme, F. P., and Otten, C. M.
    1957. The Unreliability of Blood Typing Aged Bone. *American Journal of Physical Anthropology,* 15(3):387-98.

299. Thieme, F. P., and Schull. W. J.
    1957. Sex Determination from the Skeleton. *Human Biology,* 29(3):242-73.

300. Thomas, F.
    1967. The Longitudinal Striation of the Human Nails as a Means of Identification. *Journal of Forensic Medicine,* 14:113-7.

301. Thomas, F., and Baert, H.
    1965. A New Means of Identification of the Human Being: The Longitudinal Striation of the Nails. *Medicine, Science, and the Law,* 5:39-40.

302. Thomson, Arthur
    1899. The Sexual Differences of the Foetal Pelvis. *Journal of Anatomy and Physiology,* 33(3):359-80.

303. Todd, T. Wingate
    1920-21. Age Changes in the Pubic Bone (Parts I-IV). *American Journal of Physical Anthropology,* 3:285-334; 4:1-70. Part I reprinted in 288, pages 189-243.

304. ———
    1929. Entrenched Negro Physical Features. *Human Biology,* 1:57-69.

305. ———
    1930a. Age Changes in the Pubic Bone: VIII. Roentgenographic Differentiation. *American Journal of Physical Anthropology,* 14(2):255-71.

306. ———
    1930b. The Roentgenographic Appraisement of Skeletal Differentiation. *Child Development,* 1:298-310.

307. ———
    1931. Differential Skeletal Maturation in Relation to Sex, Race, Variability, and Disease. *Child Development,* 2:49-65.

308. ———
    1942. Skeleton and Locomotor System. Chapter 12 in Cowdry's *Problems of Ageing,* 2d edition, pages 322-65.

309. Todd, T. Wingate, and D'Errico, Joseph, Jr.
    1928. The Clavicular Epiphyses. *American Journal of Anatomy,* 41(1):25-50. Reprinted in 288, pages 161-86.

310. Todd, T. W., and Lindala, A.
    1928. Thickness of the Subcutaneous Tissues in the Living and the Dead. *American Journal of Anatomy.* 41:153-96.

311. Todd, T. Wingate, and Lyon, D. W., Jr.
   1924-25. Cranial Suture Closure: Its Progress and Age Relationship (Parts I and II). *American Journal of Physical Anthropology,* 7:326-84; 8:23-45. Reprinted in *Basic Readings on the Identification of Human Skeletons: Estimation of Age* (1954), pages 265-347.
312. Todd, T. W., and Tracy, B.
   1930. Racial Features in the American Negro Cranium. *American Journal of Physical Anthropology,* 15(1):53-110.
313. Török, A. von
   1886. Ueber den Trochanter tertius und die Fossa hypotrochanterica (Houzé) in ihrer sexuellen Bedeutung. *Anatomischer Anzeiger,* 1:169-78.
314. Trotter, Mildred, and Duggins, Oliver H.
   1950. Age Changes in Head Hair from Birth to Maturity. III. Cuticular Scale Counts of Hair of Children. *American Journal of Physical Anthropology,* new series, 8:467-84.
315. Trotter, M., and Gleser, G. C.
   1951. The Effect of Ageing on Stature. *American Journal of Physical Anthropology,* new series, 9:311-24.
316. ———
   1952. Estimation of Stature from Long Bones of American Whites and Negroes. *American Journal of Physical Anthropology,* new series, 10(4):463-514.
317. ———
   1958. A Re-evaluation of Estimation of Stature Based on Measurements of Stature Taken During Life and of Long Bones After Death. *American Journal of Physical Anthropology,* 16:79-123.
318. Ullrich, Herbert
   1958. Die methodischen Grundlagen des plastischen Rekonstruktionsverfahrens nach Gerasimov. *Zeitscrift für Morphologie und Anthropologie,* 49:245-58.
319. Vallois, H. V.
   1957. Le poids comme caractere sexuel des os longs. *L'Anthropologie,* 61:45-69.
320. Vandervael, F.
   1952. Critères d'estimation de l'âge des squelettes entre 18 et 38 ans. *Bulletin du Comité International pour la Standardisation Anthropologique Synthetique* (Bologna), 25-26:1-16.
321. ———
   1953. L'identification anthropologique des mort inconnus de la guerra dans l'armée américaine. *Revue Médicale,* Liége, 8:617-21.
322. van Leeuwen, M. J.
   1948. Post-mortem Examination of Teeth and Supporting Structures to Aid in Personal Identification. *Archives of Pathology,* 46:119-27.
323. Viotti, M.
   1934. Vicios deconformação das mãos. *Arquivos de Medicina Legal e Identificação* (Rio de Janeiro), (number 10), 4:194-9.
324. Virchow, Hans
   1912a. Die anthropologische Untersuchung der Nase. *Zeitschrift für Ethnologie,* 44:289-337.
325. ———
   1912b. Gesichtsschädel und Gesichtsmask. *Korrespondenz-blatt der deutscher Gesellschaft für Anthropologie, Ethnologie, und Urgeschichte,* 43:107.
326. ———
   1914a. Halb Schädel-halb Maske. *Zeitschrift für Ethnologie,* 46:180-6.
327. ———
   1914b. Halb Schädel-halb Maske eines Negers. *Zeitschrift für Ethnologie,* 46:504-7.
328. Waaler, Erik
   1962. The Identification of the Victims of the Fire at the Stalheim Hotel in June 1959. *International Criminal Police Review* (English edition), 17:242-54.
329. Waaler, E., and Kramer, T.
   1945. [The Identification of Individuals Killed by Bombing and Explosions.] *Nordisk Kriminolteknisk Tidskritt,* 15:73-9. (In Norwegian.)
330. Warren, J. Le B.
   1955. Identification of Bodies in Mass Accidents. *New Zealand Dental Journal,* 51:22-3.

331. Washburn, S. L.
    1948. Sex Differences in the Pubic Bone. *American Journal of Physical Anthropology,* new series, 6:199-207.

332. ————
    1949. Sex Differences in the Public Bone of Bantu and Bushmen. *American Journal of Physical Anthropology,* new series, 7:425-32.

333. Webster, G., and de Saram, G. S. W.
    1954a. Estimation of Age from Bone Development. Observations on a Study of 567 Ceylonese School Children of the Ages 9-16 Years. *Journal of Criminal Law, Criminology, and Police Science,* 45(1):96-101.

334. ————
    1954b. Estimation of Age from Bone Development. Observations on a Study of 307 Ceylonese School Children of the Ages 4-8 Years. *Journal of Criminal Law, Criminology, and Police Science,* 45(2):236-9.

335. Webster, J. Gordon; Kopp, Warren W.; and Kistler, Lawrence G.
    1965. The Air Crash Medical Investigation Team. *Military Medicine,* 130:683-6.

336. Wehrli, W.
    1923. *Contribution a l'étude de l'identification par le systèm dentaire.* Zurich.

337. Weiner, J. S. and Thambipillai, V.
    1952. Skeletal Maturation of West African Negroes. *American Journal of Physical Anthropology,* 10(4):407-18.

338. Wells, L. H.
    1959. Estimation of Stature from Long Bones: A Reassessment. *Journal of Forensic Medicine,* 6(4):171-7.

339. Wentworth, Bert, and Wilder, H. H.
    1932. *Personal Identification. Methods for the Identification of Individuals, Living or Dead.* 2d edition. [First by Wilder & Wentworth, 1918], Chicago (T. G. Cooke: The Fingerprint Publication Association), 383 pages.

340. Whelton, R. L.
    1965. The Identification of the Deceased. *Military Medicine,* 130:665-8.

341. Williams, G. E.
    1954. The Identification of Persons by X-ray Examination of Bone Trabeculation. *Police College Magazine,* England, 13 pages.

342. Willis, T. A.
    1924. The Age Factor in Hypertrophic Arthritis. *Journal of Bone and Joint Surgery,* 6:316-25.

343. Wynkoop, E. M.
    1929. A Study of the Age Correlations of the Cuticular Scales, Medullae, and Shaft Diameters of Human Head-hair. *American Journal of Physical Anthropology,* 13:177-88.

Bibliographic Subject Index

Tables